Best wishes
Jannelle Jones McRee

Down on Cooter's Creek & Other Stories

written and
compiled by

Jannelle Jones McRee

Cherokee Publishing Company
Atlanta, Georgia
1986

Library of Congress Cataloging in Publication Data

McRee, Jannelle Jones.
    Down on Cooter's Creek and other stories

    Includes fiction and nonfiction.
    Includes index.
    1. Elberton (Ga.)—Fiction.
2. Elberton (Ga.)—Social life and
customs. 3. Georgia—Fiction. 4.
Georgia—Social life and customs. I.
Title.
PS3563.C7D6 1986   813'.54
86-26440
ISBN 0-87797-127-7 (alk. paper)

This book is printed on acid-free paper
which conforms to the American
National Standard Z39.48-1984
*Permanence of Paper for Printed Library
Materials.* Paper that conforms to this
standard's requirements for pH,
alkaline reserve and freedom from
groundwood is anticipated to last
several hundred years without
significant deterioration under normal
library use and storage conditions.

Book design by Charles O. Johnson
Typesetting by Graphic Composition, Inc. Athens, Ga.
Printing by R. R. Donnelley & Sons Co., Willard, Ohio

 Cherokee Publishing Company is an operating division of
The Larlin Corporation, P.O. Box 1523, Marietta, GA 30061

Table of Contents

Dedicated in
memory of my
parents,

Jannie Oglesby & Walter Campbell Jones

Acknowledgments

A special word of appreciation to Patsy A. Wiggins, whose persistence, determination, and encouragement resulted in the compilation of this book; to my sister, Neva Jones, who listened, advised, and helped me as only a sister can; to my husband, Roy McRee, who exhibited a certain amount of fortitude while I was working on the book; to Elizabeth Saggus who provided me with many photographs taken by her husband, Everett W. Saggus. A special thanks to Ann E. Lewis, Evelyn McArthur Mozley, Julia W. West, Robert Jones Thornton, Margaret Logan Herndon, Carolyn Cann, and to John Kollock, the artist who did the line drawings that appear in the book and on the book jacket. I am grateful for the help that so many people gave me.

Acknowledgment is made for permission to use articles and stories that have appeared in the *Elberton Star* and the *Elbert Beacon*, the *Anderson* (S.C.) *Independent*, the *Atlanta Journal Magazine*, the *Atlanta Journal*, the *Atlanta Constitution*, the *Greenville* (S.C.) *News*, *Georgia Magazine*, *Georgia Life Magazine*, *Georgia Stories*, *50 Georgia Stories*, *Georgia Journal*, *Antique Crafts and Gazette*, *Wesleyan Christian Advocate*, and the *Elberton Graniteer*.

The Storyteller

When people get together on social occasions, be it picnic, family reunion, holiday, it can be either enjoyable and refreshing or it can be awkward and downright miserable. What makes the difference? If someone insists on telling us his complaints, we feel it is a violation to have to live through our own frustrations as well as his.

If there is one among us with a strong personality, prestige, wealth, he may be the focal point of a group, but if things run true to form, some of us will be charmed and others bored.

Who can ensure that a gathering will be an enjoyable and even an enriching experience for everyone? A good storyteller.

A good storyteller can hold us and make us let go our own pressing concerns, and we are able to feel a sense of timelessness and richness of human experience.

The purpose of the storyteller is not just to focus attention on himself but to bring out what we all share in common. It may be all those little setbacks, from the most trivial to the big ones. One of the essential qualities of human nature is to maintain a sense of humor and a sense of balance. Humor surfaces only when events are distilled and elevated by the storyteller.

When burdens become too great, when tragedies strike, we may dislike our lot, and sometimes we may forget how much we appreciate life.

The ability to step back, look at ourselves, and see the humor in situations is one of the main qualities that can give man a true sense of dignity, neither taking ourselves too seriously nor disparaging our worth.

No one can enable us to appreciate our unique situation more than a good storyteller. —Robert Jones Thornton

A Couple of Fish Tales

It's going to be a good day if the fish cooperate.

—*Walter Jones*

Down on Cooter's Creek

If a man's got the love of fishing in his blood, that love courses through his veins as long as he lives. And that's the way it did for Walter C. Jones and A.B. Crisp of Elberton as long as they lived. Just a few years ago, before they went on to a better fishing ground, they decided to go fishing on Clark Hill Lake.

In their early eighties, the two needed cheering up. Mr. Crisp was despondent over his wife's recent death and said that he had lost his desire to live. Being hard of hearing didn't help his feelings either. Mr. Jones, better known as Uncle Walter, wasn't too happy over his failing eyesight, but they agreed on one thing. Fishing kept worry from edging up too close.

"I'll be your eyes, Uncle Walter," Mr. Crisp said.

"And I'll be your ears, Brother Crisp," rejoined his fisherman friend.

One bright spring morning in early April, the two fishermen went down to Clark Hill, better known around Elberton as the Big Lake. Mr. Crisp had a small, lightweight aluminum boat with a motor attached. As was their custom, they took their folding chairs to sit in the boat while fishing. On this particular morning on Cooter's Creek, Uncle Walter got a hard tug on his line and stood up to pull in his fish. The light boat rocked, and the two men were thrown out of the boat. As the boat spun round and round, the fishing line wrapped around Uncle Walter's legs. Eventually the fishermen were able to catch hold of the spinning boat and hang on.

"Hang on, Brother Crisp, hang on!" Fisherman Jones shouted.

"You do the same!" Fisherman Crisp yelled. "How are you making out?"

"I'm holding, but the water's cold."

"Keep kicking, Uncle Walter."

"Can't," was the reply. "Legs tied up. You kick."

From the way those two fishermen reckoned, they had held on for over two hours. They agreed, though, they couldn't last much longer. Their arms and shoulders ached, their bodies were numb from the cold.

The little motor on the aluminum boat finally stopped chugging. The gasoline supply had given out. It was quiet now on Cooter's Creek. They were too tired to call out to each other, but they were not too worn out to do a lot of thinking and a lot of praying for somebody to come to their rescue.

And Somebody did. Suddenly a strong spring wind came up and started moving the boat. The boat obeyed the instructions of the wind and moved slowly to the very shore of Cooter's Creek.

It took some time for Brother Crisp to untangle Uncle Walter from the fishing line, and it took more time for the fishermen to get their shaking sea legs used to operating on solid ground. When they struggled up, they folded their old chairs, retrieved some of their fishing equipment, and Brother Crisp found his glasses and his false teeth in the bottom of the boat.

"I can tell you one thing for certain, Brother Crisp, you *have* been living right," observed his friend.

"You, *too*, Uncle Walter."

The fishermen finally crawled into the car and sat in silence and awesome gratitude. They sat awhile and drank a cup of steaming coffee from a thermos jug that Brother Crisp had brought. When their legs and hands stopped shaking so much, they cranked up and went on the road toward home.

Late that April afternoon Mr. Crisp went over to the Joneses to check on his fishing pal. Uncle Walter was sitting in a chair by a window in the dining room. The afternoon sun brought out the blistered glow of the two fishermen's faces. Their noses were a startling red.

"Just wanted to check on you, Uncle Walter," Mr. Crisp said.

It was hard to tell which red-faced fisherman looked happier. In fact it was a grateful family circle that gathered around to hear their story.

"There's one thing I want to ask you, Brother Crisp, do you still feel like you did about wanting to die?"

A sun-red smile played games all over the face of Mr. Crisp. "No," he answered, "what about you? You want to stay here awhile?"

"I'm in no big hurry to go," Uncle Walter remarked.

Well, they stayed on awhile. Sure they went fishing again. Many times, and back to their beloved Cooter's Creek. They used their old folding chairs again and again, but not in the little aluminim boat.

1974

Fishy Doings on the Savannah

Herbert Wilcox

This is the tale of four Georgia fishermen who wanted nothing more than peace and quiet and the opportunity to prove their veracity. And the best place they knew for tranquility and easy catches was the deep, muddy water of the mighty Savannah.

Nobody seemed to believe that one time Jack Smith, Walter Jones, T.P. Wootten, and Frank Downs, all of Elberton, had caught seventy-five carp weighing from four to twelve pounds each, and that eighteen of these had been caught after supper.

On a summer afternoon they decided they would repeat this performance, not realizing that it was old home week for all the snakes. Right at the start, Jack Smith, champion fish-tale teller, reached over to tie the line to some bushes, but unfortunately he confused the bushes with a large water moccasin that bit him heartily on the finger. Luckily no preachers were around to overhear the vigorous language. After splitting the damaged finger with a pocketknife and letting the snakebite bleed profusely, Mr. Smith decided that catching fish was more important than snake venom.

Walter Jones and his fishing companion take a vote as to who's going back into the water first—the fishermen or a very friendly water moccasin.

Later in the afternoon, Mr. Smith and Mr. Jones were paddling their boat near the bank when, without so much as a casual introduction, they picked up a passenger. A tremendous moccasin fell from an overhanging tree plop into the Jones lap. Such a whoop the Savannah River never heard as Mr. Jones received his bundle from overhead, and he promptly started to jump overboard. But Smith out-talked Jones and suggested that they stick around in the cozy boat where it was all nice and dry, just the three of them.

About that time the moccasin, which was an impartial, democratic sort of squirmer, decided to cuddle with Mr. Smith, but a bateau pole broke up his plans. After getting scuffed about under Mr. Jones' robust feet and generally treated like nobody's reptile, the poor old thing gave up the ghost.

The two fishermen decided they needed rest after this bout, so they pulled up to the bank to relax. But one of them felt that he was being unnecessarily glared at, and looking overhead, his eyes met the glistening, cold orbs of a huge moccasin, a shade riled that his mate had departed to the unhappy hissing ground. In a quicker-than-thou moment the flabbergasted fishermen were on the river's other side.

Fishing then began in earnest. Just as Mr. Jones was landing a beautiful carp, he missed his footing and fell overboard, to the other three fishermen's delight. They thought it was pretty funny to see his bald head bobbing up and down in the water. It was so funny to Jack Smith that he stood up to laugh, and the boat ran against some bushes, which in turn knocked off his hat and glasses. He found his hat, but some nearsighted carp is probably having bifocal troubles.

The four fishermen decided to go ashore for a little more peace and let the fish rest. Two of the fishermen went to sleep, but Mr. Jones and Mr. Downs started in search of catawba worms. When the two sleeping beauties awoke they beheld a strange sight. Mr. Jones was sousing his bald head deep in the water, while Mr. Downs seemed to be imitating an ostrich. The worm-seekers had got a terrific welcome when they horned into a wasp nest.

These four optimists were still undaunted and convinced that nothing could mar the Isaak Waltonian serenity of their fishing trip, and they really began roping in the carp (if that's legal in Georgia). Then, the Columbus in the party discovered what he thought was a submarine on the Savannah. The submarine turned into a snooty rattlesnake that was swimming along with its head and tail up high. But the high-hat reptile was only another target for the fisherman's shotgun, and soon he was crammed into a bucket.

This is the tale of four fishermen who are still fishing—for fish and peace and quiet—and to heck with their reputation for veracity.

1946

Special People

Listen to the
quiet voices of the
country people.

—*Dorothy Nix*

Fabian Bachrach

Dr. John Ransom Lewis, Jr., poet laureate of Georgia, has received many honors and distinctions, but he will never forget the thrill of seeing his first poem in print in a school paper in his home town of Louisville, Georgia.

Dr. John Ransom Lewis, Jr., Poet Laureate of Georgia

Pure artistry may be carved with sculptor's grace and it may be in the shape of a poem or a painting. But according to Dr. John Ransom Lewis, Jr., poet laureate of Georgia, it can just as well emerge from the oven in the shape of an old-fashioned apple pie. He believes that in every living being there is a song of the heart that needs to be more than an echo.

From the time that Dr. Lewis, a noted plastic surgeon of Atlanta, was made poet laureate in 1972, he has set aside each Friday to do all he can to kindle a love for poetry. Over the years he has driven thousands of miles to talk to students ranging from kindergarten to graduate-school age.

When he is invited to a school, poems spill all over the place—on walls, blackboards, posters, and even on poetry trees. After his visit to Harry H. Epstein School in Atlanta, he received a special gift dedicated to him: *The Epstein School Anthology: A Song for All Seasons.*

Little children and big ones grown tall listen to the poet laureate's poems and to poems written by his favorite authors. And in a time of sharing, Dr. Lewis turns his ear toward their talents and encourages them in their creations.

By the time the poet laureate was able to take charge of a pencil, he began writing poems that his eighty-seven-year-old mother still keeps as prize possessions. From early childhood he knew that he wanted to be a doctor like his father and a poet like Robert Louis Stevenson. And when a young boy wills to do what he wants to do, something is bound to happen.

Literary accomplishments have piled up high for Dr. Lewis, but he will never forget the thrill of seeing his first poem in print in a school paper in Louisville, Georgia, his home town. Two books of poems have been published by University Press of Washington, D.C., *To Dock at Stars,* published in 1962, and *Small Town,* published in 1976. His next volume of verse,

Dragons Are Lonely, whimsical in form, will be a collection of children's poems. His poems have appeared in more than a dozen anthologies of southern literature. The poet laureate feels the need for Georgia poets to be recognized, so a new anthology will be published under his direction this year.

He recalls the pleasant memories he has of his first grade teacher, Mrs. Louise Ramsey of Louisville, Georgia. "She was a true scholar and she understood children." In his book, *Small Town,* there is a poem entitled *First Grade Teacher.* He writes: "We know so late the things you taught / were more than books could hold."

As a child the poet laureate had frequent attacks of asthma that temporarily prevented him from playing baseball and football. Fortunately an Augusta specialist prescribed exercise as a means of overcoming asthma, so young John Lewis resumed his place on the football and baseball field, and the doctor's advice proved sound. So sound that the young athlete was offered two major-league contracts and also a college education as a bonus. To his parents' relief he did not accept the major-league offers. Now he realizes that his illness had its own compensations. It gave him an opportunity to read. He considers Robert Louis Stevenson "a true physician-poet because Stevenson helped many young children feel happier and as a result healthier when they read his classics."

The poet laureate's ancestry provides an extra bonus for genealogy buffs. On his father's side he is a direct descendant of Robert E. Lee and Jefferson Davis, and on his mother's side he is a direct descendant of Daniel Boone.

In the beginning Dr. Lewis practiced general surgery, but he later decided to be a plastic surgeon. Now he has limited his work to aesthetic plastic surgery. At first his father disapproved of this decision, but he soon told his son that "it is just as important to make people happy as it is to make them well, and in many instances you are doing both."

As a writer of poetry and prose, who can cut through verbiage better than a surgeon? According to Dr. Lewis, there is a bridge between surgery and poetry, for in poetry one finds the breath and spirit of all knowledge.

Those who know him personally and professionally know that the physician-poet's greatest happiness comes in helping someone. A friend of Dr. Lewis said, "Neurosurgeons have told me I'll never walk again, but then along comes an article that John Lewis sent me about paralyzed victims who were determined to walk again and who succeeded. I believe in a man who does not give up."

A graduate of Emory University Medical School and Straith Clinic in Detroit, Michigan, Dr. Lewis is the author of *The Surgery of Scars,* a technical book for surgeons. In his second medical book, *Atlas of Aesthetic Plastic Surgery,* he writes: "All of plastic surgery is both science and art. . . . The plastic surgeon, perhaps more than any other physician, should have at least a working knowledge of both classical and modern art and sculpture. . . ." His third medical book, *The Art of Aesthetic Plastic Surgery,* will soon be published by Little, Brown and Company of Boston.

Not only has Georgia's poet laureate lectured on poetry in various areas of the United States, but he has lectured on plastic surgery and has demonstrated surgery in many parts of the United States and in numerous countries of Europe, Asia, and South America.

On May 2, 1981, Dr. Lewis flew to Athens, Greece, to lecture to the European Confederation of Plastic Surgeons. From there he went to Cairo, Egypt, to lecture to the International Society of Aesthetic Plastic Surgeons. But flying to Greece and to Egypt to give five lectures did not prevent his arriving on time on May 1, 1981, to talk to the fifth-grade students at Twin Oaks Elementary School in Lawrenceville. In the past two years the fifth-grade students have published more than sixty books. The children's response to the poet laureate was something to remember. Their enthusiasm and applause may have meant even more to Dr. Lewis than the standing ovations he has received after he has given medical lectures.

Recently the poet laureate participated in a program at a psychiatric hospital. "It has been one of the most satisfying programs. . . . One of the psychiatrists and some of the nurses there said that during the latter part of my program some of the patients began to communicate better than they had seen them the whole time that they had spent in the hospital. I also received a letter from them as a group and a request for books of poetry which I have tried to help them get."

The physician-poet does most of his writing late at night, or when he is on trips. "I dictate my prose on a tape recorder, for I can think very well when I am dictating prose." Even traffic jams provide him with extra time to dictate prose for his medical writing. "I can only write with pen and pencil when I am doing poetry. Many of my better poems have come very rapidly, but other times they have not come out of the subconscious at all and I have to write and rewrite them."

A man who requires only four to five hours of sleep a night, Dr. Lewis has this to say: "It is important to sleep an adequate amount without overdoing it. There are so many things to enjoy. Enjoy them. Mind affects matter. . . . There is some power greater than I, and I know that it is God." In *Day's Immortality* he writes:

> I feel an awed expectancy as day's
> Last breath is drawn, the slowing pulse
> > grows still.
> The gauze of dusk wipes up the crimson
> > stains
> That mortal wound has smeared on
> > rumpled clouds
> And puddled in the west. A grandeur
> > still
> Remains through all the quiet fading
> > light,
> And stays to gild the drapery of night.

Dr. Lewis admits he has a great deal of energy and ambition to keep pushing ahead. "I wish I knew how to slow down and relax but I continue to push forward." With a trace of a smile he said, "I am sure when I leave this earth I'll want to stay a little while longer to get something done."

For a lover of the perfect word and of order and beauty Georgia's poet laureate tells how he would like to be remembered:

When I am poet to the courts of sleep
I hope some mortal bards will say of me:
He writes with zest but with humility.
His pen knew not the words to make us
    weep,
Nor yet to make us laugh aloud or long,
But simple words that give the heart a
    song
And send us softly smiling to our sleep.

1982

Turkeys Can Be Beautiful!

There is an old saying that Rayle, Georgia, is the only place in the world where a man can make a living and not hit a lick of work. But the Callaway family has taken a different stance. Eugene and Avola Callaway and their two sons, who live on Cross Road Farm, raise a half million turkeys a year, and their White Leghorns lay over a hundred million eggs a year. A lot of work is involved in caring for these turkeys and chickens.

The Callaways live in a home that was originally a two-room log cabin built in the 1820s. Cabin Hill was a gift from Eugene's grandfather, Adolphus Sanford Richardson, and three attractive and useful additions have been made.

Douglas Branan

Three generations of the Callaway family: Mrs. John Callaway, center, with son Eugene and his wife, Avola, and grandsons Eugene, Jr., and Blake.

The Callaway sons, Eugene and Blake, are the seventh generation to live on this farm, which is part of a 1781 land grant to their forefathers, who moved to Wilkes County from North Carolina.

It is easy to feel the close bond with the past at Cabin Hill. On the porch there are invitations to linger awhile: a white wicker swing, rocking chairs, and an old church pew. In the hall an ancient wardrobe receives the wraps and coats of guests. An old broad ax on the wall is a reminder that it once hewed out the cabin logs. A two-hundred-year-old Blaisdell clock ticks away in the hall. Pictures show the original cabin with its overhead beams just as they were at the turn of the eighteenth century, along with each addition.

Throughout the home there are pleasant reminders that the Callaways are in the poultry business—pictures of turkeys, a turkey-shaped basket for magazines, china Buff Orpingtons from Italy, and English china with a beautiful turkey design.

An old ox yoke holds the overhead lights in the den. School desks with many names scribbled on them are used as end tables. Upstairs is a beautiful brass bed that Avola found in a shelter on the plantation.

It was Eugene's mother, Mrs. John Callaway, the former Elizabeth Richardson, who really started the poultry enterprise. She is called the Nancy Hart pioneer of the poultry business. She got into this venture when times were hard, money was short and their middle son, Alan, had a serious heart condition. She found that the greatest alleviator of worry was hard work.

So back in the 1930s, it all started with chickens and eggs, and from the beginning the enterprise was a success. She was soon supervising the work of ten employees. The poultry pioneer provided dressed chickens for Oliver General Hospital in Augusta and the Fort Gordon dining room and Officers' Club. Nothing was automatic in those days. Everything was done by hand. At that time they had eight hundred layers and sold eggs in Athens and Augusta as well as locally.

"When we first began our poultry undertaking, Eugene showed great interest and he saved what he made. He always wanted to make money, and he usually managed to have change in his pocket. He used to grow turnip greens and supply the neighboring stores," recalls Mrs. Callaway.

After graduating from the University of Georgia with a degree in poultry, he married Avola Whitesell, of Lewisburg, Tennessee, a graduate of Cornell and a former member of the University of Georgia faculty. He went into the commercial egg business with his brother, Dolph, but Eugene found that there was more money in turkey production, and today he is the largest turkey producer in Georgia. At present he is working hard to establish a turkey processing plant in Georgia.

Mrs. John Callaway lives next door, and she recalls how different things used to be. In earlier days, most families were extremely fortunate if they boasted a turkey at Thanksgiving and Christmas. One year she and her husband had a turkey, but they needed another, so they bought a gobbler from a Negro who lived three miles down the road. The gobbler disappeared from the Callaway Farm, so John Callaway went looking for the bird. He asked the Negro if he had seen his lost turkey. "Lawd, Mr. John, I got him right here. That turkey done come home."

It has been said that turkeys are the least intelligent of all birds, but over the years the Callaways have learned a lot about them. On the range, a flash flood won't hurt them too much, but a prolonged rain may prove disastrous. Sometimes from 50 to 100 percent of the turkeys will be lost.

"A turkey may not have sense enough to come in out of a shower of rain, but it does have sense enough to find its way home. But what the Lord doesn't put into his head, you can't hope to." So says the pioneer of the poultry business.

Eugene Callaway has discovered that turkeys are the sliest of all birds, and because of this trait and their acute hearing, wild turkeys are much harder to kill than the fleetest of deer.

According to Oscar Taylor, foreman of Callaway Farms, turkeys have the curiosity of a nosy neighbor. They walk up to people and inquisitively circle around them, but they are stubborn as a Georgia mule. They can be led, but they cannot be forced.

Bill Wilson

Blake Callaway, shown here, and his brother, Eugene, are the seventh generation to live on Cross Road Farm, and their father, Eugene, is the largest turkey producer in Georgia.

When one-day-old baby turkeys are delivered from a North Carolina hatchery, they require close watching for several days. The young birds pile up in a knot and can be easily smothered. Consequently, for the first few days and nights, Mr. Taylor and other employees stay with them until 9 or 10 P.M. They put a few to each brooder to avoid trampling and suffocation.

"Turkeys are a sight to see when they are from ten to twelve days old," says the Callaway foreman. "We remove the wire pen and let them have the run of the houses. Sometimes thousands of turkeys make a straight run of more than a hundred feet. They look like a sea of billowing white waves. At other times, they march as if they are in military formation. There's no sight to equal it."

On Callaway Farms there are no dull moments for any member of the family. In addition to her role as mother, homemaker, decorator, and church, school and civic leader, Avola Callaway is also a culinary expert. An immense kitchen and a banquet table in the dining room provide ample space for entertaining.

It is a good thing that turkey is a year-round standby and not just reserved for the holiday season; for, on a moment's notice, friends and business associates fly in from faraway places to Callaway Farms.

At Thanksgiving and Christmas, Avola and her mother-in-law prefer to serve the traditional turkey dinner, but at other times, favorite recipes for turkey and crabmeat or turkey enchiladas, or their sons' favorite, barbecued turkey on grill, may be served.

The Callaway family takes pride in living on the land of their forefathers. It has never insulted Mrs. John Callaway to be called a country woman. She has done her share of milking cows, churning, and digging in new ground. Her greatest loves are country life, flowers, fishing, and all the things that pertain to the good earth.

Avola shares the same love of the land and its limitless heritage. And she is adept at doing the expedient thing. When egg distributors of Callaway Farms became ill, she went to work. Someone remarked that Avola Callaway was the only egg peddler in Wilkes County who had a master's degree.

The Callaway sons know what discipline means. Of course there is time for hunting, swimming, fishing, and horseback riding, but there is also time for work. They load turkeys and look after their horses, cattle, and dogs. They are deeply attached to the land of their forebears, and they intend to stay on the farm as past generations have done.

Mrs. John Callaway admits that Georgia's biggest turkey producer has far more patience than her father had. "I remember when my father needed to have a plow repaired. The shopkeeper had closed up, so my father went to a neighborhood store and bought three yards of black calico. He made a big black bow and tied it on the front door of the store. He said, "If a man's not on duty, he's the same as dead."

So the Callaways stay on duty in spite of an awesome number of time-consuming commitments. One of the quotations on their kitchen wall strikes to the heart of this family: "It seems the harder I work the luckier I get."

1976

Everett Saggus

Betty and Bill Lester of Elberton have been honored many times for their service to the community.

Chickens and Good Deeds

When Betty and Bill Lester of Elberton went into the poultry business, they started from scratch. They knew nothing about raising chickens, but they knew they were dealing with their favorite food, especially when fried.

Their first year of raising broilers on consignment was a big success, but the next year was a failure and they had "to borrow money to quit." They began selling processed poultry to independent stores and supermarkets. They bought a truck and hired a driver, and when the driver didn't show up, Bill drove. If the truck broke down, Betty proved to be as good a mechanic as she was a bookkeeper. In the lean years of the 1950s, the Lesters cut up the chickens, packaged them, and helped to load the truck.

Today Bill Lester, president of Elberton Poultry Company, sells to and buys from poultry processors throughout the United States, and exports frozen poultry to countries all over the world. Their local delivery, within a seventy-five to one-hundred mile radius of Elberton, includes poultry, canned goods and more than three hundred frozen foods.

When folks work hard, keep their promises, and try to help their fellow man, the news gets around. The Elberton Foods Industries honored Bill Lester for his guidance and support to their program of youth activity. In 1975 the Elberton Chamber of Commerce presented him the Small Business of the Year Award for the Tenth Congressional District and, two years later, honored Betty and Bill for "their contribution to the agricultural business industry in our community."

Their church and civic activities are many. Betty helps Bill in his work as president of the Elbert County Unit of the American Cancer Society. He is also Lieutenant Governor of the Georgia Optimist Clubs, having served as president of the Elberton club. Betty is president of the Alpha Rho Chapter of Beta Sigma Phi, and in February of this year she was named their Valentine Queen, a very special honor for a grandmother.

The Lesters believe that strength comes from work. Whatever they have accomplished has come from hard work and keeping promises.

1978

The Dean of Massey Hill

Bill Massey made it possible for many University of Georgia students to work their way through college by enrolling in the Massey Hill Jughead University located on his farm at Nicholson. Students who wished to live on Massey Hill Farm were interviewed and carefully screened before they were accepted. Low rent was charged in exchange for help on the farm, and the houses were basically furnished by Massey. He was particularly interested in young folks who had no knowledge of farm life, and he called them his *jugheads*.

The Dean of Massey Hill Jughead University grew up on a farm, and he learned to plow a straight furrow behind a mule when he was barely able to see over the plow stock. Farm hours began at daylight Monday and lasted until dark Saturday.

According to Bill Massey, Marie Staton of Jefferson was his very first jughead. When Bill and Marie married in 1944, Marie became acquainted with back-yard "conveniences" and drawing water from a well on the back porch. Her social activities included cooking for the farm workers and driving a pickup truck across the fields, instead of driving her father's Buick in downtown Jefferson. So Bill and Marie became well equipped to introduce city-bred students to working on a family farm.

Jugheads Bill and Alicia Hames gave Massey Hill Farm another name, The R.W. Massey School of Hard Knocks (like it or not). They gave a detailed description of available courses, which included Gardening and Bush Hogging, Animal Doctoring, Carpentry and Construction, Plumbing and Electricity, and African Engineering. A course in Domestic Life covered yard upkeeping, trash and junk disposal, and house upkeep.

In Carpentry and Construction, Bill taught the ancient secret of how to make a short board longer. He advised, "Don't ever measure before cutting a board, just look at it and cut it. The more things a board has been used for, the stronger it is. The uglier a finished job is, the better it is."

African Engineering afforded a number of practical ideas. A jughead learned that old tire tubing, twine from hay bales, and tenpenny nails can be used to fix anything from an auto transmission to the space shuttle. Massey emphasized that thousands of so-called worthless pieces of junk should be saved for all the custom jobs.

The English language was acceptable at Massey Hill Jughead University, but it became apparent that since the Dean called something other than its proper name, it was necessary to learn the *Hill* vocabulary. The Dean's system of grading was summed up in eight words: *You know when you've done right or wrong.*

Ginny and Graham Liles and their son Trey of Milledgeville lived at Massey Hill Farm in 1974 and 1975. Graham referred to Bill as *Chief.* "He was not unlike the head of a tribe that lived on his reservation. He made the rules, we followed the rules. He helped provide food and lodging (through his community garden, his livestock and his cheap rent). All he ever expected in return was friendship, respect, proper behavior, and some good hard work.

"When I would get home I would help him mend fences, build or repair other houses on the property, plant and tend his garden, cut and bale hay and other chores he would assign. He was always tough but fair and treated me and my family just as if we were his children."

In many ways, however, Bill Massey was far from tough. When Jake, one of Mark Hall's best hunting dogs was about to die, Bill suggested that Mark use the rent money to pay the vet.

A. H. Rackley of North Ridgeville, Ohio, said that Bill taught him how to be sensitive to the needs of other people. "He had a way of sensing just when we were short on money. He'd tell us to pay only half our rent or to forget that month's rent altogether. The last three months we were there, Bill wouldn't charge us any rent at all because he wanted to make certain we had the necessary money to relocate to my job after graduation. When I would tell Bill "thank you" for his help, he would always say that the only thanks he wanted was for me to help somebody else.

"Bill taught me that being a good businessman requires nothing more than using good common sense. He believed that regardless of the problem, there was always a simple answer. You just had to use a little *horse sense.*"

These are some of the things Massey's students learned to do: How to guide a plow, how to shape a plow, how to split hickory logs for fence posts or ax handles, how to fix leaky pipes with tire inner tubes, how to install a commode, how to set up electric fences, how to dull a sharp nail so it won't split the wood, how to worm cattle, and how to drive on a muddy road without tearing it up.

Mike and Marsha Floyd learned from Bill Massey that "if it can't be fixed with a rubber inner tube or a wire coat hanger . . . it can't be fixed."

There are many things to remember about Massey Hill Farm besides mending fences in the moonlight and herding cattle back into the pasture at three o'clock in the morning. Coon hunting on a cold winter night, walks through the pasture along the creek, sitting around the kitchen table and eating Marie's delicious baked beans, visits to Bill's cabin in the mountains and listening to him tell about how it was when he grew up.

Arnoldina Davis, a friend of the family, said that almost every morning there would be more than one jughead to appear just about the time that Marie's biscuits were ready to come out of the oven.

When the time came for a jughead to leave Massey Hill Farm, he was expected to talk to the Dean about his future plans. In most cases the Jughead degree was not conferred because the Dean felt the work was never completed.

"I never got my *formal* degree from Massey Hill written down on paper," said Mark Hall, "but I found out some things, helping your neighbor, being fair with folks and sharing. It's worth all the formal education I ever had."

On Father's Day in June 1985, Bill Massey received an unforgettable gift, a book of letters written by his jugheads. These expressions of love and appreciation were compiled by Clifford K. Potts and Martha Massey White.

And on Monday afternoon, February 24, 1986, there was a special section reserved for the jugheads at the First Baptist Church in Jefferson. They came from far and near to honor Bill Massey and pay their last respects to a friend who had taught them far more than how to plow a straight furrow.

1986

Harry Whelchel

Bill Massey made it possible for many University of Georgia students to work their way through college by enrolling in the Massey Hill Jughead University located on his farm at Nicholson. Massey was particularly interested in young folks who had no knowledge of farm life, and he called them his jugheads.

Judge Thomas and His Second Wife

as recalled and told by Thelma Wright Payne

My Aunt Cora Thomas Tate told me many stories about her father, Judge Thomas of Augusta. This was in the 1800s. After Aunt Cora's mother died, Judge Thomas married again, and the new Mrs. Thomas had all his little children to look after. One day the Thomases were expecting guests, and Mrs. Thomas planned on having a good time. She told the children, "We're going to have company, and I don't have time to wash your dirty little faces. Don't you children come out. Just stay in the back. We'll just sit on the porch awhile. They won't be here long."

No sooner had the guests sat down than these dirty little faces started appearing at the front door.

With sympathy and endearment Judge Thomas said, "Come to your daddy, you poor little motherless children."

Mrs. Thomas, extremely small in stature, sat as tall as her diminutive body allowed and said with more than conviction, "Judge Thomas, *no one* regrets the death of your first wife more than I."

* * *

Way back in the 1800s, flour and meal were bought by the barrel, and crackers were bought in cases. Weevils were often found in the flour, meal, and crackers.

Mrs. Thomas had a dinner party, and the dining room table was beautifully set with her finest linen cloth. During the meal little weevils appeared and started crawling on the linen cloth. As Judge Thomas tried to get rid of them he quipped, "Like Samson I have slain my thousands."

"Yes, Judge Thomas," retorted his little wife, "and with the same weapon—the jawbone of an ass."

* * *

Because the second wife of Judge Thomas of Augusta was so small, he teased her to a breaking point. When he came home, he often asked her if she had done certain things. Mrs. Thomas would reply that she couldn't do it because she couldn't reach it. The husband said, "You're so little you can hardly do anything."

The wife countered, "I'll have you know that precious jewels are done in small packages.

Reply by Judge Thomas: "Yes, and so is poison."

* * *

Judge Thomas was always bringing guests home to eat and sometimes his wife got tired of it. On this particular night she had a beautiful table adorned with crystal, silver, china, and fine linen and candles on the table. The guests had been there a long time, and Mrs. Thomas just kept on talking. After awhile, Judge Thomas said, "Well, Mrs. Thomas, don't you think it's time for dinner to be brought in?"

The diminutive lady answered, "Judge Thomas, when you called, you told me to have a *light* supper and not a dinner, and I've got *every candle* in the house on the table."

Judge Thomas pushed back from the table and said, "Come on, boys, let's go eat in a hotel in Augusta."

The Mule Trader, a Short Story

I hadn't been around too long before I found that you had better not skin a Georgia mule dealer unless you are prepared to have your own hide nailed to the barn door.

A mule trader just naturally begins early. When Jed was twelve he bought what he considered a beautiful bull calf. I remember the great gleam in his eyes as he led his animal home. When he told Pa the price he paid, Pa said a little sad-like, "Son, you went too high."

Jed straightened up to his sixty inches and said, "Maybe so, Pa, but he'll grow to it."

Jed had a white-faced Hereford that I wanted. I figured a little trading between brothers might pay off. I had a beautiful horse I wanted to get rid of. You see, she was a blinker. In case you don't know what that means, a blinker is a moon-eyed animal who has good eyesight at a certain time of the moon and poor vision at other times. So one day I asked Jed if he'd be willing to swap his cow for my horse. Jed was blunt.

"Bud, my cow won't suit you."

I finally convinced him that nothing could suit me better "It's a deal, then," he agreed and we made the trade.

As he climbed on the horse and picked up the reins, I said a little too casual-like, "Jed, at a certain time of the moon you might watch your horse carefully. His eyes. . . ."

Jed leveled a straight shot look at me. "Thank you, Bud. And there's something I failed to tell you. If you expect any cow juice it might be wise for you to get the strongest oak timber you can find to build a stall. The cow you just inherited is the world's worst kicker."

That finished me in the trading business, but Jed went on from there. Some liked him and some cussed him.

One night when Jed was eating supper, someone knocked hard on the door. When he opened it, there stood Jake Bellows. Jake's mouth was playing shake and twist. Beside him stood a mule with his head aimed low.

"Jed Barker," Jake trembled, "you handed me a dirty deal. I've had this mule a month, and she won't do a durn thing. What are you going to do about it?"

The mule dealer pondered. He looked at Jake. He inspected the mule. "Jake, I don't believe you quite understand the full significance of your situation. By the way do you have a horse?"

"No," snapped Jake.

"Well, it just so happens that you are luckier than most mule owners. You see, you've got what is known as a high-brow mule."

"What the dickens is that?"

"It's when a mule becomes more than a mule. When this happens, there's no use trying to make him plow. He wants to be a saddle animal, and

I tell you that a saddle mule is something your neighbors will talk about. Think it over, Jake. You know my motto—'If you like the mule keep him and pay off. If you don't, bring him back.'"

Weeks went by, but Jake did not return. As far as I know, Jake is still riding that high-brow mule.

Ma didn't want Jed to bet with anybody, much less Tom Simpson. Tom said Jed bragged too much. "Any fool would know that all the mules you ever sold wouldn't remember you," Tom argued.

"Why, Tom, not only do they recognize me but they do what I tell them to do."

"All right, we'll make a trade," said the unbeliever. "Let me pick out a mule you've sold, and if he knows you and does what you tell him to do, I'll give you fifty acres of the best bottom land in Elbert County. But if you lose I want six of the best mules in your barn. Shake on it, Jed?"

"I'm willing," said the trader.

"Well, they traveled all over Elbert, Hart, Wilkes, Madison, Lincoln, and Oglethorpe. Finally they found a twenty-two-year-old mule that Jed had traded years before. Jed walked up to her and stroked her head. "Hello, Hattie. You're the best trainer of green mules I ever had. Remember when you had a sore foot. I nursed you for six months."

Hattie snuggled on Jed's shoulder.

"Humph," snorted Tom. "What does that prove?"

"Take it easy, Tom. Hattie," Jed said gently, "go to the branch, get some water, eat your dinner and come back to your plowstock at one o'clock."

Hattie obediently went to the branch, drank some water, ate her dinner, and at one o'clock she backed up to the right plowstock. Finding the right plowstock was something in itself since there were ten identical ones in the field.

Nobody thought Jed would ever find a woman. He didn't show them the proper attention. I would say he looked about as good as brothers usually do. All the girls liked him and the womenfolks too. When a woman buys a mule, wouldn't you say she was interested in the dealer as well as the deal? Well, Jed sold more mules to women than any other dealer this side of the Mississippi.

His world went around in a spin the day Sadie Higgins moved to town. He bought a tailor-made suit and parted his hair on the other side. Some bet Jed wouldn't get Sadie, but the folks who had traded with Jed figured he would win. He started dropping by to see Sadie, and he'd sit till bedtime. Word got around that Jed proposed to Sadie one night but she turned him down. Sadie didn't seem to take much stock in mule dealers. It seems she wanted a professional man.

I believe Jed was cut up over Sadie, but he buckled down and sold more mules. Ma and Pa advised him to slow down, but their son had a mind of his own.

He didn't seem scared when Jim Limkins cornered him in the livery stable and leveled a gun at Jed and shot his hat off.

"Anything wrong, Jim?"

"You've sold one mule too many," Jim roared. "Just one ornery stubborn cussed mule too many."

The dealer in mules picked up his hat, rolled it around and inspected

Even presidents have to bend over to tie their shoes.

—Margaret Swift Whorton

the hole. "Jim," Jed countered, "if a mule's master is sensible and intelligent, the mule is too. If the mule packs a mean wallop in its hind legs, he's only kicking up for his rights. Look in the mirror, Jim. What you see is what your mule is."

"What are you talking about?"

"Just this. Whose footsteps can a mule follow but his master's? Watch your step, Jim. Your character might be showing."

With that, Jim jumped on Jed and knocked him flat. Jed rose slowly. I've often wondered what would have happened if one of Jed's mules hadn't taken over and kicked the daylights out of Jim.

Jed might not have gone to Texas if penicillin had been discovered. He shipped fifty mules to Missouri, and all of them died of pneumonia. Of course there was talk around the corner drug that half of Jed's heart was aching for Sadie and the other was grieving for the four-legged critters.

The old town didn't have the same feeling with Jed gone. Men grumbled and found fault with Preacher Wilkins, and Preacher Wilkins promptly brought their weaknesses into focus.

The first Sunday the new preacher came, I went to church and sat where Jed used to sit. Sadie Higgins looked around, hopefully, I thought, but when she saw me she opened her Bible and bowed her head. I had a feeling that she was praying for the return of a dealer in animals that have no pride of ancestry nor hope of posterity.

The mule trader came home the next year, a little older and a lot richer. His tall tales turned a dozen men toward Texas, but Jed settled down to the mule business in earnest. He got to be such an authority on mules that he wrote a book about them called *Tips to Mule Traders,* but that book didn't give away my brother's real trading technique.

One night Jed was invited to make a speech on brood mares. I have a feeling that Jed knew Sadie was sitting on the back row. "You ought to choose a brood mare," he said, looking carefully over the audience, "like you would a woman. There are four things to keep in mind: first, her blood; second, her frame; third, her state of health; and fourth, her temper."

You might say that was a right unique way to propose but it worked anyway. Jed and Sadie got married during a slack mule season. On their first wedding anniversary they exchanged gifts. Sadie presented Jed an eight-pound son who just might grow up to be like his father. And when Jed presented Sadie with a high-brow mule, I knew for sure that specifications had been met and approved.

Miss Sybil

Miss Sybil did not assert herself. Consequently you could not go to her and ask an opinion. She would dally with words and wait to see which limb you were on. Then after you had taken your stand, you could depend on her to agree with you. Miss Sybil was an asset to the community, for who is there who does not want to be heard or to be agreed with?

I wonder what made Miss Sybil the way she was. Was she the second child who had to give in to the firstborn? It could have been her appearance. Her hair drooped where it should have tilted upward. It had no definite color. An artist might have called it ash on ash. Her eyes were neither blue nor brown. They had flecks of gray, yellow, and several indefinable colors.

Being agreeable has its comforts, but as I remember, it also can present problems. Especially when friends and foes are gathered together under one roof. Well, it happened just like that. Miss Sybil got so befuddled she almost took a stand. Instead she followed Thoreau's advice and went to the woods.

Embarrassment did not stop her. One night at the Civic Club, she was asked to give a report of the program committee. She stood up and fingered the notes she held. No sound came. She cleared her throat, smiled, and looked around. By then her audience was suffering far more than she. When she finally sat down, the speaker of the evening arose to the occasion. He did choose a timely subject, *The Magic of the Spoken Word*.

When someone died, Miss Sybil was the first one to call or come or write. When she came to extend her sympathy, you felt that she was probably nearer the departed spirit than any other mortal.

I have misled you if you think that Miss Sybil was a spinster. She had quite an array of husbands. They came in all sizes, tall, short, thin, bulgy. They lived, they died.

I, grown old, am beginning to see why six men sought her. If I had been a man, I probably would have been the seventh. She did not kill the men she took in sickness and in health. She merely agreed with them.

Undoubtedly their demise stemmed from total agreement.

If she had just raised one argument, Miss Sybil might have a husband today.

Janie Allen Remembers

As a teacher in a one-room schoolhouse for thirty-three years in Elbert County, I was once asked what my duties were. I said I was principal, teacher, lunchroom supervisor, nurse, janitor, playground supervisor, and counselor.

One lady wanted to know how I felt about teaching in a one-room school. I told her I was proud of it. If I were not proud of what I did, how could I teach children to feel proud of the school and their place in it?

My school to me and to most of my pupils was just one big family. I was the mama who loved each one and who was interested in them. In most cases they loved in return. When children came to our school they usually looked forward to coming. Why? They and their parents knew that I *wanted* them. It was important to be wanted. Shirley, age five, came to me at a Home Demonstration Club meeting and said, "Miss Janie, I bet you'll be glad when I start to school."

I never knew what I would be called on to do. I visited several old people in our community who did not attend church. Well, one died. The funeral was to be at the home. Some people gathered there. A preacher from another county, we were told, was supposed to come and conduct the service. We waited and waited and waited. Finally, a man came to me and said, "Miss Janie, you will take charge, won't you?" I thought—always new things happen. Just when I was about to say something, the preacher showed up—to my relief.

When my students needed someone to laugh with, I laughed; when they needed someone to cry with them, I cried. I shared their pleasures and

Janie Allen, Elbert County schoolteacher, has fond memories of her years in a one-room schoolhouse.

their sorrows. I taught the children all week at school, and on Sunday I went to church and played the piano. I played at funerals and at weddings. I rejoiced when new babies arrived, and I felt proud when they graduated from high school. I met with the Young People on Sunday night and enjoyed Vacation Bible School in summer.

One little boy in my class felt that he had an important job. He walked and went to school so early. His mother wondered why. He said he had to go and make the fire and get it warm for Miss Janie.

We had a piano in our schoolroom. I bought it cheap. Most children are never happier than when they are singing. Many doors are opened and many lessons are learned through song.

Several summers we had a summer session for eight weeks, and then we dismissed so that the children could help with the gathering of crops. Our school was located near the church. When the time came for the week of the revival, we all walked over to the church. The children came to school all cleaned up for the occasion. We helped with the congregational singing, and we sang special songs. Bobby, age eleven, sometimes did not remember to be quiet, and Jim, age six, was a little wiggle-tail. Before we went to church I asked Bobby to sit behind Jim and to punch Jim if he got too restless. Bobby accepted his responsibility, and Jim kept on guard.

I remember two children who moved into our community. They had never been in a church. In class we talked of George Washington, "the Father of our Country." Also each morning I read or told a Bible story. I had talked of our Heavenly Father many times. One little boy got mixed up. I asked who could tell me something about George Washington. One of these little boys raised his hand. "I kin, Miss Janie. He was the Father of our Country, and he died on the cross to save us from sin." Of course I had *more* teaching to do.

Questions constantly arose. One child said, "Miss Janie, Daddy says we ain't *on* this big round world—we're inside it. If we're on it we'd fall off." Another lesson to be taught.

My tasks were varied. Many times a mother sent Johnny's eye drops to be used every three hours, Mary's tablets for a stomach disorder to be taken every four hours, and Bobby's poison oak medicine to be applied as often as I thought necessary.

Years ago Susie, age eight, moved into our community. In the community where she had lived, the mother sent her to school, but the teacher sent her home. The next year she started to school but was sent home again. I welcomed her to our school and tried to assure her that she was wanted. With watery eyes she stood and stared. I soon realized that she could not see well. I offered to try to get help if her parents gave their permission. I went to the welfare office and was promised a certain amount. I then went to an eye specialist, and he made me a special price. I took Susie and her parents to town to the doctor. It was late before we were able to leave town, and the Christmas lights were turned on. Susie had never been to town at night and had never seen Christmas lights. The joy that was brought to Susie gave me one of the happiest Christmases I have ever had. After medical help she improved and became a happy member of our school family.

One morning just before time to ring the bell to open school, I saw coming down the hill toward our schoolhouse a man carrying a kicking,

In every family there are stories of favorites parents have picked among their children. I could never believe in that. All of us love one person more at some time or other, usually according to his needs. But on the long haul, we love equally, each

crying boy. The man brought the boy to the door and said to me, "Here is Billy, my little brother. He don't want to come to school."

Billy was eight years old and had never been to school. I reached out and took what was brought to me. I caught him around the waist, because I could not have held him with one hand. I assured the big brother that Billy would be all right, so he left. Billy quieted down and gave no trouble the rest of the day. With the children's help and interest, we soon made Billy feel that school was where he *did* want to go.

When Billy returned to school after a summer vacation, he was pale and had lost weight. He did not write as well. He told me he could not see out of one of his eyes. His brother took him to an eye specialist, and as soon as he could get up one hundred and twelve dollars, he could have his eye "fixed." I thought it looked like a cataract, which it was.

Every few days Billy said they couldn't seem to get enough money to go. The next day I contacted the welfare office.

Early the next morning at school a man knocked on my door. He had been by the welfare office and had been told about Billy. The parents were notified to take Billy to the hospital, which was one hundred miles away.

The Welfare Board furnished money for transportation. I secured some necessary clothing from the Empty Stocking Fund in town. After the examination and operation, Billy's worries and dread ceased. The case to the state was a thousand-dollar job, which was little to pay to make a little boy feel secure. Billy wasn't fully prepared for his next grade, but he had done the best he could with what he had. I promoted him with his group, and I felt confident that he could succeed.

Our little one-room schoolhouse was the first school to have a lunchroom in Elbert County. We were also the first in Elbert County to have a lunchroom under the Government School Lunch Program. Lunches were provided for those who were unable to pay and for others whose parents were able but would not.

I shall never forget a little boy who was submerged with problems. Fortunately nature was at our door. A walk in the woods was an opportunity to study plant life, animals, birds, and trees, and more importantly a place of discovery of self. For a long time it seemed impossible to reach this young child, but one day after the sun rose to its highest, my little troubled child went walking through the woods to bring me wood violets, little pitchers, hepatica, trumpet flowers, and evening bells. Years have passed, but I can say simply and truthfully, he is my friend.

To many people a graduation invitation is a dun. To me it is Bill's recognition and praise for him. It's my pleasure and privilege to congratulate and remember him. When he wants a character recommendation for a job or school or for other reasons, he honors me by asking me to write it. I know Bill's good points, and he knows that I know them. It is his praise of me.

But Bill, in spite of overanxious parents, uninterested parents, and a deficient teacher, comes through. If he has been made to feel that he is able to help himself, that he has a place to fill and a job to do, he *will* succeed.

Author's note: Janie Allen's teaching career has spanned forty-nine years.

child is as dear in his way as his brothers and sisters. We need something different from each—laughter from one, practical common sense from another, fierce loyalty from the third and so on.

—Celestine Sibley

Sarah Adams and Her Wise Old Owls

Carolyn Cann

Sarah Adams, who now has more than three hundred owls in he collection, started in 1958 with an owl salt-and-pepper set her mother gave her.

A large ceramic owl from Mexico stands guard as protector of the flower and vegetable garden of Mrs. Sarah Dye Adams in Elberton. Another owl welcomes guests to the patio where owl chimes give a musical greeting to those who enter the Adams "Home of the Owls."

Mrs. Adams, who now has more than three hundred owls in her collection, started in 1958 with an owl salt-and-pepper set her mother gave her. Large and small, her "birds of wisdom" have come from England, Hong Kong, Italy, and India, and include owl music boxes she bought in Tokyo. They are made of pine cones, walnut shells and seashells, candles, strings, felt, sequins, ceramics, stained glass, crystal, brass, and copper. Owl pictures run the gamut from wire and nails to macrame and crewel embroidery.

There are seventy-five owls in the kitchen. Her night light is a hoot owl, and she has earbobs, pins, and pendants in the shapes of owls. They have dominion over the bathroom—towel holders, towels, soap, and wise old birds in the window.

Her love for owls began in childhood on an Elbert County farm when her brother found a baby barn owl and placed the soft feathered bird in her hands. Years later during sleepless nights, she and her invalid mother living in a wooded area of Elberton listened to the strange cries of the barn owls, the hoot owl, and the trill of screech owls. To them, the songs of the owls seemed to have a quality that soothed the spirit. Thus a hobby was born.

When Christmas comes and then her birthday on January 6, gifts of more owls from children and grandchildren will add to her collection.

1979

Ruth Hunt and the Wagon Wheel Antique Shop

If you want to live the best life of all and meet the best people, get into the antique business. But be sure you have a son that will stand by you and love it too. So says Ruth Hunt, owner of the Wagon Wheel Antique Shop in Elberton.

Thirty-five years ago Mrs. Hunt and her eight-year-old son, Gerald, opened an antique shop in a little garage beside her home on North Oliver

Street, and the whole town was invited for homemade cookies and their favorite drinks. The town turned out and folks bought many odds and ends, bric-a-brac and a bundle of aprons that she had made. One word of advice from the entrepreneur: "If ever you want a crowd, just serve them something."

"Some time later a friend called and wanted to buy more aprons. I told her I couldn't make any more. My antique business was growing so fast. At first I didn't know a thing about antiques. Later I realized I was raised up with antiques and didn't know it."

Two years after opening her shop, a member of an Athens Garden Club asked her to have a booth for a week at the old Georgia Hotel. Ruth had bought a pine cupboard for $2.50, and during the week she brought barrels of glassware and china to fill her cupboard. Many of the people who had booths told her to up her prices. Ruth Hunt's answer: "I believe I'll sell it like it is."

She loves pictures almost as well as she loves books. She has pictures of Betsy Ross, the Birth of the American Flag, and the American Girl of '76. She and Gerald have a new display of more than five hundred pictures that they have collected. One conversation piece is a large mural of Nancy Hart getting the best of the Tories. It was painted by Fred Bradbury of Hart County. She may consider selling this painting, but only to a Georgian. Today there is far more room to display these treasures. The Wagon Wheel Antique Shop now includes eight additions, plus another house next door.

Years ago Mrs. Hunt paid seventeen dollars for one thousand books packed in trunks and cedar chests. Today she cannot count the thousands of books that she has in her antique shop, but she knows that she has one of the finest collections of southern literature, with particular emphasis on Georgia.

In addition to her great knowledge of antiques, Ruth Hunt is known for her knowledge of the early history of Georgia. She has trunks full of old records of Georgia, and many people come to her for help in research. She has contributed a number of valuable antiques to the Elbert County Historical Society. One of her gifts is a rare pine huntboard.

In the beginning the antique owner had very little money to invest, but she saved up enough money to buy a dresser from Noah's Ark in Abbeville, South Carolina. When she went to get the dresser, the owner of Noah's Ark showed her far more lamps than she had ever seen. He told her he had no room for them, and he would let her have all the lamps for twenty-five dollars. Ruth Hunt left Noah's Ark without the dresser, but with enough lamps to light all the way home. She and her son hung the lamps all over the ceiling and in every conceivable place. Did she make a profit? You bet she did. The price of each lamp: twenty-five dollars.

There is never a dull day for Mrs. Hunt. She recalls the time that an Elbert County sheriff stopped an old man driving a pickup truck loaded with old fruit jars."

"Let's go to the police station," ordered the sheriff. "No," said the old man, "let's go to Ruth Hunt's. And that's exactly where the sheriff went. He was surprised at what he found—Ruth Hunt's Wagon Wheel Antiques—no still, but a warm inviting home chock-full of antiques.

Recently Mrs. Hunt decided to add a wing or two to her home. Son

Ruth Hunt says her ingredients for success are simple: a lot of work, a lot of luck, and the help of the good Lord.

Gerald said, "Mama, surely you're not going to do any more building at your age." Mama Hunt, who turned eighty in October 1982, took no time in replying, "I most certainly am. If I don't live in it but one day, it will be worth it."

For the current trend, according to the Wagon Wheel owner, everybody wants oak. "It will stay with you forever. I have plenty of walnut and teakwood, but oak is what they want. And wicker, there is no way to supply the demand. One of the most sought-after pieces of furniture is a round oak china cabinet, and grandfather clocks are way out of sight. The other day a man came in to check on a beautiful grandfather clock that he had been admiring for some time. He said, "Well, I see it's still here.""

"Yes," quipped the owner of antiques. "The longer it stays here the more it goes up."

One antique collector said this about Ruth Hunt: "She has the *most real* antiques around in this country. And I'm not talking just about the Southeast either. I've told many people that if you can't find it at Ruth Hunt's you might as well stop looking."

No wonder she has customers from every state in the union and Canada, and no wonder she has received international recognition. Her home has the charm of a storybook land: teaster beds out of an old plantation, rare books, all kinds and colors of glass, dolls, chairs, tables, pictures, clocks. . . .

Her antique shop is a meeting place for old friends and new acquaintances who come from everywhere. Nearby friends used to come in on Sunday afternoons and sing. Her preacher told her it was sinful to keep her shop open on Sunday, but she allowed that she kept a lot of people out of devilment.

Who are her best customers? Young people. If they cannot afford what they want, their parents will come to their rescue and make the purchase.

The name of Ruth Hunt is synonymous with giving. When little children come with their parents, they don't leave empty-handed. If they find a doll, basket, or trinket that they like, the antique owner is another Santa

Claus. She loves to see their eyes grow big in wonder and happiness. And she reminisces, "Many of my *children*, now grown, come back year after year and bring their children and grandchildren and remind me of what I gave them."

Elbertonians know the beloved antique owner for what she believes. And that is simply to help those who need help. She finds out about folks who need food, clothing, beds, mattresses, and wood. She has probably given away more than she has ever sold. And if those who come to her for help need more than she can provide, she knows someone to call to get what is immediately needed.

Her ingredients for success are simple: a lot of work, a lot of luck, and the help of the good Lord.

Someone who left her shop without buying the rocking chair she really wanted came back saying, "As I was going down the road, the Lord told me to come back and pay ten dollars down on that rocking chair and pay the rest in two weeks."

Mrs. Hunt allowed that the Lord might be about more important business. Nevertheless, she made the sale, conceding that the Divine One just might be aware of the comfort of a rocking chair.

1982

Miss Lola, Elberton Seamstress

Could you sew for the public for more than three score years and ten and still have a gleam in your eye? At seventy-eight could you still get all fluttery inside when you sewed for a bride? Mrs. W. A. Reagan, better known as Miss Lola, of Elberton, not only has made countless wedding gowns, but she has many people who depend on her to do all their sewing.

"If you don't mind waiting your turn, I'll get to you as soon as I can," is her usual answer to the dressmaking question.

For forty-eight years Miss Lola has had the same machine, a Wheeler Wilson head and Singer stand. "I believe an electric machine would run away with me. With this I can pedal to suit my moods."

At the age of four, little Lola found a needle and thread more fascinating than toys and boys, and her mother was soon convinced that her daughter was not too young to sew. When the child was ten, she began sewing in earnest.

The dressmaker recalls the bright-some-time-ago-days when relatives or neighbors would drive up to her house and cart her away to do their season's sewing. And oh, the dresses, petticoats, corset covers, and old-fashioned drawers that diminutive Lola made in those high-ceilinged rooms of yesterday.

The Elberton designer frankly admits she prefers sewing for teenage girls. "They don't have any cantankerous isms. But the saints protect me from an adoring husband who tags along to see if his wife's dress hangs right. He just ought to hang."

Cheap black material sends shivers skedaddling all over Miss Lola. "Give me something lively, monkeys riding bicycles, but deliver me from dull stuff." And, off the record, if you want a dress finished in jet-propelled time, buy material in a soft shade of yellow, and your dress is practically on your back.

The problems of the old and young never fail to interest the dressmaker. "I just listen and sew and wish I could help in some way. All I can do is try to understand."

1949

Rachel Whitmire Photographs Children and Animals

Rachel Whitmire agrees with Mark Twain, who said that if you pick up a starving dog and make him prosperous, he will not bite you. She also has found that one sure way of never being prosperous is to pick up strays, pay vet bills, and choose photography as a hobby.

As a child Rachel wanted to be an artist like her grandmother. She has never painted pictures, but she has done her share of taking them. She took her first picture with her grandmother's camera, a Brownie 2-A. She felt like a millionaire when Eastman Kodak Company awarded her a prize for her picture of a kitten in a box.

Children and animals are her greatest loves, and her photography is largely focused on them. Her concern is shown as she brings new life to the East Point Child Development Center and helps the Atlanta Humane Society find good homes for discarded animals.

The southwest photographer has probably tied up, slowed down and stopped more traffic than any woman in Atlanta. When drivers see her pick up an injured or abandoned animal, they don't blow their horns—sometimes they offer their assistance. One night on her way home she saw a dog that had been run over. The dog was too heavy for her to lift, but a young gentleman came to her rescue. At the nearest telephone she waked up her faithful veterinarian, Dr. Tommy Allen, and between yawns he agreed to meet Rachel at his office. Nine weeks to the day, Floogie, the purebred "cur," presented Rachel with a special gift—seven puppies.

The photographer's gifts seem to come in swift succession. One day as she was driving along, she saw a kitten disappear into a sewer. She slammed on brakes, went across the road and called, "Kitty, Kitty." Not only did one lone kitten emerge from the sewer, but three soft bundles of fur followed their leader. Their kitten compass had directed them to a certain lady who understood their language.

Whatever the language, child or animal instinctively responds to Rachel Whitmire. When she was asked to photograph a four-generation family, a four-month-old baby kept squalling long and loud. The exhausted photographer said, "You've talked your baby into feeling sorry for himself. Now don't be alarmed or surprised at what I do." So she stamped her foot, clapped her hands and yelled, "Shut up!" The baby did as he was told, plugged up a sob and turned on a whopping big smile.

In the classroom she has fun with the children. Several years ago the intelligence of pigs was being studied at Harris Street School in East Point, so Rachel took Rosebud, a Poland China pig, to a fifth-grade classroom.

Photographer Rachel Whitmire says that children and animals are her greatest loves. She achieves a "double exposure" in one shot with this photo of twins Bill and John Clendenen.

The children went wild with excitement, but Rosebud maintained her calm and took directions in English and Spanish.

One cold, rainy day a friend called Rachel and asked what he should do with a bear cub that he had found on the road in north Georgia. Her advice was to look for its mama. When he discovered that the mama had been run over by a truck and killed, Rachel said, "Then pick him up and bring him on. I'll find him a mama and a home."

Soon Puddles, the seven-pound Georgia black bear cub, made himself at home in Mama Rachel's kitchen, back porch, and big back yard. When he wanted bread he got his own toast out of the toaster. He liked all fruits, and each day when he decided on Coke time, he would go to a carton of Coca-Colas and bang on the door. Puddles preferred to drink his Coke straight from the bottle. He liked to have his food served with a fork and spoon at the table.

No doors can be opened wider than the doors of this animal lover's home in southwest Atlanta. Friends and strangers who go on vacation call her to keep their pets. A recent guest for a week was a squirrel, but sometimes guests are like the man who came to dinner. A raccoon spent a year. Puddles spent two years. At one time thirty cats depended on her for food and lodging, but now her family includes three abandoned cats—Sweetie, Siamezie, and Kat—who have been with Rachel for ten years, and Flopsie, an English sheep dog, that she found on the roadside two Christmas Eves ago. Flopsie was a shivering, frightened puppy trying to dodge a truck.

The fearless photographer has had many close calls taking pictures of tigers, ocelots, lions, and cougars. But she has always been rescued by the attendants at the Atlanta Zoo and the Stone Mountain Park Game Ranch.

In describing Rachel, a newspaper columnist said, "She prefers children and animals to a Cadillac." And truly she does. What a gathering it would be if Rachel Whitmire could watch a parade of all the babies, children, grownups, and animals that she has photographed and befriended!

1979

James Hester and his friend Tessa share a special moment together, captured on film by photographer Rachel Whitmire.

Jessie Banks

Just about everybody in Elbert County knew Jessie Banks. She was black and proud of it, and she was proud that both blacks and whites had a genuine affection for her. If ever there was a living soul who loved everybody, it was Jessie. "I've lived a long time," she once said, "and I've found out that lovin' all is forgivin' all, and I pray for the whole wide world."

She believed that anger was a fearful weapon. "No matter how mad you get, hold your tongue and watch your step," she advised. "Whatever you say is permanent and you can't take it back. Just use that riled up feelin' to clean your house, plow up your garden, and plant some collards."

Her love for children and animals made her a favorite babysitter for babies, children of all ages, and family pets. Children who have long since grown to maturity recall the tall tales that Jessie told.

Often times the parents would leave the children at Jessie's house, especially in the spring. The children believed in her stories of hidden gold, and they dug where Jessie told them to dig. As spring slipped into summer,

*Children believed Jessie Banks'
stories of hidden gold in Elberton,
and they dug where Jessie told them
to dig. As spring slipped into
summer, the hidden gold in the
garden took the shape of row on
row of beans, corn, tomatoes,
squash, and cabbage.*

the hidden gold in the garden took the shape of row on row of beans, corn, tomatoes, squash, and cabbage. When Jessie's little friends stopped by to see her they said, "Jessie, you told us if we dug hard enough we'd find gold."

"I told the truth," she replied, as she gathered a basket of tomatoes. "*This* is God's gold."

Jessie had no children, but she *adopted* every child she looked after. Jessie told her little folks about wee people who lived in attics. Because of her tall tales, many an attic in Elbert County underwent constant investigations.

She had a red shawl that she had crocheted. She called it her magic shawl, and she said if you wore it, your wish would come true. One child who put on the shawl was convinced that it was magic. She wished that her parents would go somewhere so Jessie could be her babysitter. Her wish came true.

Jessie believed in keeping promises, but at times it was no easy task. One afternoon when she was looking after twin girls who were five years old, she told them that she would eat a handful of dirt if she failed to call up a doodlebug before sundown. Jessie did a lot of calling before the setting of the sun, but no doodlebug came to her rescue. And no matter how difficult it was, she ate a portion of the good earth.

How she was available to so many people still remains a mystery. She was no registered nurse, but she was registered in the hearts of people whom she cared for. It was an old saying around Elberton that any season of the year was a good time to stay away from the doctor, but if you did get sick, Jessie Banks would nurse you back to health in no time.

There was a special reassurance about Jessie praying for someone. Her faith was absolute. Her prayers seemed to have a special priority when it came to reaching on up to heaven. When someone asked Jessie for her prayers she said, "You know I'll pray for you. It's my duty. Now quit that worryin'. God's got gumption. He knows what it's all about."

Before Jessie went on to plant a celestial garden, she made a promise to this writer. She said, "I'm goin' before you. I think it's best." She was asked why. She answered, "I'd better go first so I can help pull you in." What a comforting thought—to be pulled on in by good old Jessie.

When folks asked Jessie what her love was like, she said, "My love is like a hydrant. I can turn it either off or on."

One love she never turned off was her love for Rose Hill Baptist Church. Years ago when her church was destroyed by fire, she made a promise that she would give all she could to rebuild it, and with a steeple, too. Her vow was fulfilled. On Highway 78 East a few miles from the girlhood home of Corra Harris, Rose Hill Baptist Church was rebuilt and with a steeple. It is often referred to as *Jessie's church* and *Jessie's steeple*.

1985

Sara Finney, the Wood-carver

On Hard Twist Ranch near Milledgeville, Sara Finney makes wood carvings so real-looking that her fruit and vegetables have been refrigerated and, according to local dentists, sometimes bitten into. Her birds are so lifelike that cats stalk them.

From childhood, saws and hammers held far more appeal than dolls and laces, and she made name plaques and whatnot shelves for family and friends. She began painting in oils and, five years ago, exhibited a number of paintings of landscapes and horses.

A new career began the day she stopped at the Sanford House in Milledgeville and left a bread tray full of fruit and vegetables carved in wood. By the time she reached home, her telephone was ringing, and art dealers at an antique show wanted her price list. She admitted it was pretty high since she could not produce enough to be practical.

In 1965 she carved her first bird, the quail, then the meadowlark. Since then she has carved most all of the common songbirds, and quail and duck also. For mounting she uses driftwood, dried limbs, and sometimes unusual roots.

Tut Finney

Sara Finney makes wood carvings so real-looking that her fruit and vegetables have been refrigerated and, according to local dentists, sometimes bitten into.

"My workshop is my favorite place," she says. "It is Granny's old smoke-house. The old farm bell still hangs that she clanged every morning to rouse the workers to go to the cotton and corn fields. Now these fields are growing coastal bermuda for my white-face cattle, and folks are driving up in the yard to ask if this is the place they can buy some wood apples."

Recently a man came to buy some wood apples. He did not know that Sara Finney also carved red peppers and strung them. On leaving he noticed the peppers hanging on the wall and remarked, "Your garden surely did produce a lot of peppers this season." He was amazed when he found that the peppers were made of wood.

Hard Twist Ranch has earned a new name, *Bird Watchers' Heaven*. A pair of pileated woodpeckers come right up to the door to eat pecans. In an old limb hanging over a creek are Sara Finney's favorite birds, the prothonotary warblers. Her brother Tut made some houses and took them to the swamp, and the warblers nested in them. Tut hung the boxes or houses over the water, as their natural nest was. All up and down the creek are nest boxes for birds. They resemble oatmeal boxes. It was a day of celebration when a tufted titmouse and her mate gave final approval to one of these boxes and built their nest.

Orders have come from Canada, Nova Scotia, England, Scotland, and Germany. But far-flung places do not hold as much appeal for her as home folks in Georgia. When the chartered Greyhound bus from Decatur brought the Grandmothers' Club, thirty-five strong, that was the day!

In the kitchen of the old governor's mansion in Milledgeville will lie the wood-carver's greatest triumph—a selection of carved fruit and vegetables, a memorial of love in memory of the late Miss Mary Thomas Maxwell, professor of English and former dean of women at Woman's College.

"She believed in me," says Sara Finney, "and like my family she spurred me on. What art success I have achieved comes not so much from talent as hard work and the support of good friends. I have just been lucky and happy. So here I am."

1970

Author's note: In recent correspondence, Sara Finney reports, "My business has advanced from working with a pocketknife to getting my wood from North Carolina by way of an eighteen wheeler. I now have three buildings, a studio, a sales room, and a saw shop. My workshop used to be in Grandma's old smokehouse. Fortunately, my brother, Tut Finney, and my sister, Martha Lou Finney, have gone into business with me." Sara's carvings are on display in the Georgia Room of Constitution Hall in Washington, D.C.

Baby Heavyweights

Mr. and Mrs. T. O. Bond of Elberton sadly admit that they are slipping. On September 13, 1944, their seventh child, Terry Julian, made his squalling entrance to this muddled universe to the tune of ten pounds and three ounces, and the Bonds are mystified at his scanty weight, especially since their other six children weighed from twelve to fifteen pounds at birth.

Meet the Bond babies in the order in which Mama and Papa Bond met them. Mary Evelyn weighed twelve pounds at birth. Oliver Martin weighed fifteen pounds. Next arriving on the scene was Curtis Leroy who weighed thirteen pounds. Nadine weighed twelve pounds, and Annie Lenier weighed thirteen pounds.

"It's just natural for my babies to weigh a lot," Mrs. Bond declared, "because my mother had ten children, and three weighed ten pounds and the rest of them weighed eleven and twelve pounds." Mrs. Bond herself weighed twelve pounds at birth.

"All my children have been perfect specimens," the mother proudly admitted. "They have not even had a blemish of any kind." She attributes their perfect health to their being the breast-fed variety.

"Plain food agrees with children," according to Mrs. Bond. "With the last three babies I have fed them on baby food after the first nine or ten months, but the others ate fatback, sorghum, cornbread, pot likker, and all kinds of meats and vegetables, and they couldn't have been healthier."

The father, a polisher at a granite shed, is one of eight children. Up until last year he was a painter, but he admits that he has thrown away his paintbrush and bucket. No one disagrees with him when he says that he has a full-time job satisfying the hunger and wants of seven children.

Doctors are fine when they are needed, but Mrs. Bond sticks to the old-fashioned home remedies. Her most popular medicines are syrup of black draught for plain green-apple stomach ache, castor oil, and minute doses of calomel and soda.

"My husband believes that castor oil can perform miracles," laughed Mrs. Bond, "and he pours it down the children. But if it's left up to me I give them something else."

"My children are my flower garden," she continued. "I don't have time to dig in a rose garden when I have so much digging to do for my family."

"And as for sewing," she added, "there is no time do do any sort of needlework except darning socks and patching torn-up pants."

"After a woman has as many children as I have she doesn't tear her shirt when they are out playing. I let the older ones look after the younger ones and the saints be with them if they go to sleep on their job. A mother gets sort of immune to bruises, stumped toes, and bloodcurdling yells if she has a big family."

"My ambition," Mrs. Bond said, "is to raise all my children to be fine men and women and put them through school so they can make their own way. But—as for any more babies—I have plenty."

1945

Lots of miracles are performed by simple hard work.
—S. Truett Cathy

You Can Always Tell a Georgian

Three young women recently drove into a filling station at Jacksonville Beach, Florida, in a car that bore a South Carolina license plate. Immediately a man with a broad grin and a big, black cigar sallied forth and said, "You know, it's wonderful to see three lovely girls from Georgia."

The flabbergasted young ladies, who were indeed from Georgia, demanded to know how Bill Touchton could tell that they were from the Empire State of the South when they had come riding into his place in a car from the Palmetto State. So Mr. Touchton explained things by putting on a little act. He closed his eyes and clapped his hand down on the driver's head, but he wasn't confusing her with the radiator. He was merely getting warmed up to tell the befuddled one at the wheel where she first saw the light of day. After he had told her exactly where she was born, she carefully avoided asking him when.

According to the guessing specialist, it is easy to spot a Georgia cracker. "You can tell a Georgian by what he does with his hands. A Georgian, be it man or woman, starts reaching in his pocket for money or starts opening a pocketbook or a billfold. I haven't decided whether they are anxious to pay for the gas or whether they are wondering if they have enough money to pay for it, but they do reach for the money before they order. Now the women usually reach for a comb and start arranging stray locks of hair and more than likely they whip out a compact. The men are equally busy straightening out their coats and yanking on their ties. All Georgians invariably smile, and whether they are pretty or pretty awful looking they lap up flattery."

The mental banker's psychological study grew out of experience rather than schools. His plans for a formal education were upset by his father's illness, so little Willie Earl Touchton of Valdosta, Georgia, started kicking around for himself early in life. His keen study of people resulted from his ambition to be an old-style drummer with a big cigar. "I learned through conversation with people, and I think in this way I gifted myself with knowledge."

Georgians are a complete giveaway with their first question. On driving up they always ask, "Where's a good place to eat? Easterners ask, "Where's a good hotel?"

Some time ago a man drove up, and Bill Touchton said casually, "It's awfully nice to see Atlanta people, and especially a big executive." The man was astonished, for he was from Atlanta and he was the head of a large firm.

When his customers drive off it's a goodbye, a smile, and a drop me a card, won't you. First he tried to keep his cards in a neat collection, but now they spill out of everywhere.

Besides knowing too much about people, Mr. Touchton has two hobbies, smoking stogies and dancing. With two correspondence courses in dancing to his credit, he can cut the rug and he has taught dancing in his spare time. "But," he says, "my wife and four children are hobby enough."

In Miami he received the nickname of "Windy Bill"—and deservedly. Once while traveling with a clothes salesman, Bill Touchton made one sale too many. It was the day he sold a woman a suit of clothes for her just departed husband. The inspired salesman, however, sold the suit with an extra pair of pants. When the story bounced back on him, Bill had a ready comeback. "Well, you see the widow has already picked one of the pallbearers for her next husband, and the future groom is in a dressing room seeing if the pants fit."

The term *southern hospitality* was born in Georgia and South Carolina, in the opinion of the Florida operator. "Of all people, they are the nicest, the most congenial, courteous and understanding. It really isn't hard to tell them. The old saying is true that you can see the high water marks on them."

1945

David Dean Rusk

Waiting to see the dentist can provide more privilege than pain, especially when it provides the privilege of meeting Dean Rusk, the former secretary of state, and now the professor of international law at the University of Georgia in Athens. When I asked him if he was who I thought he was, he answered with a smile. And when I asked him if I could come and talk with him sometime, he graciously agreed.

On June 7, 1983, I received a letter from Mr. Rusk saying, "I would be glad to visit with you here in Athens sometime if we can find a mutually convenient date. I would suggest that you call Ann Dunn who will try to work something out with you. . . ."

That did it. Dean Rusk said he would be glad to *visit* with me! To this would-be writer a visit sounded a whole lot more comfortable than an interview. When I told my sister Neva Jones about the letter, she was so excited, she wanted to go with me. And when I told our neighbor, Margaret Swift Whorton, who lives down the road in the woods, she said, "Oh, if I could only go and shake his hand!" So I called Ms. Dunn to see if it was all right for them to come, and it was.

On our way from Elberton to Athens we bought some early June peaches for Mr. Rusk and his secretary. The peaches were correctly named, for they were picked too early in June. As we walked toward Mr. Rusk's office, my better judgment advised me to give the strange fruit to the campus birds, but I didn't.

The professor of international law at the University of Georgia is a lucky man. He has a secretary who has charm, poise, and self-control. Anybody who can accept those peaches with grace and a straight face is a born actor. And so is Mr. Rusk. Standing in the doorway to welcome us, we couldn't tell what lay behind that smile as he looked at us and the fruit.

But I can say this. When we walked into his office he did more than shake our hand. He made us feel warm and welcome. Just like Georgia home folks.

He turned back the pages to his early years. He was the fourth of five children born to Robert Rusk, a Presbyterian circuit rider preacher, and to Frances Clotfelter Rusk, a former school teacher. He was born on a one-horse farm in the Lickskillet District of Cherokee County, Georgia, in a house that his father built. It was the first house in Cherokee County to have glass windowpanes. There were three rooms, a bedroom for his parents, the second bedroom for the children, and the third room served as kitchen, dining room, and living room. The well was on the front porch.

Mr. Rusk's family is Scotch-Irish. Four generations of his family have spanned the life of our country. When they gather together for a reunion in Cherokee County, he is reminded of his deep Georgia roots. In the family graveyard on the Georgia homestead is the tombstone of his great-grandmother, who was born in 1776.

David Dean Rusk, professor of international law at the University of Georgia, has enjoyed a life of distinctive achievement. He was born in Cherokee County, Georgia, and grew up in the West End section of Atlanta. His mother and father instilled in him the meaning and practice of goodness and truth, loyalty and courage, and a deep abiding faith in God.

For years Julia West was known as ordinary of Elbert County. She is now judge of the probate court in Elberton. She still receives some mail marked Ordinary. When Louis Campos delivered her a letter which was addressed to

Because of a throat problem, Dean Rusk's father could not continue his duties as a preacher. He moved his family to Atlanta. His family first lived in a frame house where Georgia Tech has now taken over. Then they moved to West End, along the Central of Georgia railroad. He remembers a switching station, a firehouse, an icehouse, and a syrup factory, and nearby there was an industrial dump, where a child could find material to build almost anything. It was such a pleasant place to live and, adding richness to the neighborhood, was a library adjoining the Wren's Nest, the home of Joel Chandler Harris, author of the Uncle Remus stories.

Early on, young Dean assumed his share of responsibility. When he was eight years old, he got his first job at a grocery store next to the icehouse. He took orders for groceries and delivered them in his little red wagon, and he was paid three dollars a week in pennies.

Mr. Rusk recalls that his father was strict in substance and rather gentle in manner. When asked if he ever got a paddling he said, "Oh sure. My father had a leather strap called "Billy." When we misbehaved he used it." His mother left the administering of "Billy" to Robert Rusk.

He attended an open-air school for the first three years. He passed examinations and entered school in the second grade. To insure warmth the children had woolen bags to put on over their regular clothing. Every hour they would get up and take exercises. Every three hours the students were served hot chocolate. It was a fine school with highly trained teachers. When Dean was in the fourth grade he appeared before the Board of Education to testify in favor of continuing with the open-air school. Another classmate, Katherine Hunter, (Mrs. Harllee Branch, Jr., of Atlanta) childhood sweetheart of Dean Rusk, was also one of the five or six students to appear before the Board of Education. The children did not have colds in the winter, but in spite of the healthy condition of the students, the petition failed.

He attended Boys High School, where the highest academic standards were maintained. His Greek professor, Preston Epps, was one of his finest teachers. "He lighted our fuses with great ideas. Later he became a Keenan Professor of Classics at the University of North Carolina. He died in 1982 at the age of ninety-three."

When Rusk was at Boys High, he received the Atlanta Journal cup awarded each year to the Best All-Round student. The late Dr. Joseph Boland was a co-winner of this award. During Rusk's senior year at Boys High he was the editor of a school page in the *Atlanta Journal.* His pay was forty dollars a month.

After graduating from Boys High, he worked for two years in a law office so that he might make enough money to go to Davidson College in North Carolina. At Davidson he worked in a bank, waited on tables, was bookkeeper and student manager. Work goes hand in hand with achievement, for he was elected to Phi Beta Kappa.

From Davidson, Rusk went on to study at St. John's, Oxford, as a Rhodes Scholar. After completing further graduate work in England and Germany, he returned to the United States and studied international law at the University of California. His plans for a teaching career materialized when he became an associate professor of government and dean of faculty at Mills College in Oakland, California. Virginia Foisie, a history and geography major and a scholarship student, signed up for Rusk's course in international relations. His course was informative and obviously persuasive, for after Virginia Foisie's graduation, the professor and the student were married in June 1937.

His teaching career was interrupted by World War II. In 1940 he entered the army as an infantry reserve captain, becoming colonel and assistant chief of staff in the Burma theater. As he moved on to become a political expert at the War Department, his career in public life took on greater dimensions. He joined the Department of State in 1946, and this career ultimately resulted in his appointment as Secretary of State from 1961 to 1969, during the Kennedy and Johnson administrations.

As I sat listening to David Dean Rusk, I could see the indelible imprint of parental influence. His mother and father instilled in him the meaning and practice of goodness and truth, loyalty and courage, and a deep abiding faith in God. They gave him hope and encouragement, and they taught him to work physically and mentally to reach the ultimate of his talents. His parents taught by example rather than words. His environment emphasized the importance of being an individual and the right of each one to have space to grow and go on from there.

"I remember my father chanting Psalms in Hebrew," said Dean Rusk. "He gave a certain resonance and beauty to the Psalms that I shall always remember, and I was intrigued with that. From early childhood we committed to memory large sections of the Bible.

"The Sabbath day was a special day for us. On Sunday we memorized Bible verses. We went to Sunday School, to church Sunday afternoons. We could go walking in the woods and visit the family on Sunday, but we could not read the funny papers until Monday."

Mr. Rusk said that during the Cuban missile crisis he could not help but think of the first question of the Westminster Shorter Catechism: *What is the chief end of man?* and he recalled the answer: *To glorify God.* . . . . . .

When difficult times pile high he adheres to the circuit preacher: "Pray as if it were up to God; work as if it were up to you."

I shall remember him standing in the doorway to welcome us into his office. With Rusk there is a courage that balances talent. I see in his eyes a hope for peace. He is a teacher with an open door. He listens, advises, and shares his knowledge. I am glad that David Dean Rusk came back home to stay.

1984

The Reverend Harper Heard Reminisces

I attribute my long and healthy life to one word, *behavior.* No one has ever been able to make me do something against my will and better judgment. I have never fasted in all my life. Why should I when I have been temperate all the time?

I have done many things. I have plowed, split rails. I've done all farm

"Ordinary, Elberton, Georgia," Miss Julia noticed that the word Ordinary *was crossed out and the word* Special *was written in ink. As Louis Campos handed her the letter, he said, "Beyond a doubt there is nothing* Ordinary *about you."*

work except use a cradle for cutting grain. I have kept a daily diary. I've been keeping my shoulders in tune with the other fellow. In my life the way I have come is the most blessed way for me.

I believe in short sermons. No more than thirty minutes. A preacher can go round and round, and if he keeps on going around, you forget some of the rounds. I was licensed and ordained to preach in 1906.

To love, the heart has no room for anything but love. Hatred in my life does not exist. If I can't love you because you don't love me, then I am weak. It makes me puny if I love you only if you love me. I accept the fellow who rejects me. I'll lean over backwards, go out on a limb, even if the fellow would like to see the limb break.

Some people think we are approaching a new day, but we are living in a new day. It has come.

I concentrate on events. I remember word for word the newspaper articles written when President McKinley died. I remember the sinking of the Titanic in 1912 just as if it were yesterday. I can recall verbatim every recorded event I read about Leo Frank. I have a photographic memory. I have been invited to speak to the history students at the University of Georgia. Dr. Emory Thomas was the teacher. They wanted to find out why I had such a good memory and what made me tick.

There were books all around the room where I talked. There were many students. Dr. Thomas said, "Students, if you used your head like Reverend Heard has used his, look at all these books around the room. Your head would be more valuable than all these books."

I've been pushed up so high and I've been trampled so low. I have had many privileges in Nicaragua, Guatemala, and Central America. In the 1920s I worked with Georgia Baptist missionaries.

At times in my life I've been resented by many petty things. I've also been resented by my own race.

I taught in a high school near Hartwell when the radio was just appearing on the scene. I picked up a friend and I told him what a radio could do. He said, "I think you're one of the biggest fools."

I turned on the radio. The message from Hartwell stated that a Dr. Hailey had just died about an hour ago.

I said, "You ought not to believe what you just heard, but we'll ride on to Hartwell and see what has happened to Dr. Hailey."

The man found out. The doctor had just succumbed.

The radio was the real thing. I had worked for Atwater-Kent in Philadelphia in the early days of radio.

Some of the school patrons said, "I'm going to take my boys out of that school where he teaches. He's got a hole in his head."

I believe electronics will change the course of history, just like man going to the moon.

I don't think we are doomed.

I am now coordinator of all Elberton churches. I am associate minister of Rose Hill Baptist Church. I thank God that I'm the oldest preacher in Elbert County. Sixty-nine years of preaching.

My plans are to stay here at least a hundred years. Take my advice: Eat plenty of turnip greens and don't take medicine.

Joseph C. Mills

The Reverend Harper Heard advises, "Eat plenty of turnip greens and don't take medicine."

In my life the way I have come is the most blessed way for me.

1975

Author's Note: The Reverend Harper Heard died in 1977, two years after this interview. He preached seventy-one years. He was a member of Rose Hill Baptist Church, where he served as assistant pastor, a member of the Elberton Ministerial Association, past vice-moderator of the Savannah River Association, retired teacher and principal in the Elbert County School system, and a veteran of World Wars I and II.

Everett Saggus, Master of Photography

Everett Saggus

Master of Photography Everett Saggus of Elberton has come a long way from the Petit Studio in the backyard of his family home in Crawfordville to being elected to the Royal Photographic Society of Great Britain. This eighty-two-year-old honor society was incorporated under Queen Victoria's sponsorship and is currently sponsored by Queen Elizabeth the Second. Today its world membership numbers only 2,032 photographers.

From early childhood, Saggus expressed his creative talent in many ways. He found great pleasure in lying on the grass and looking up at the clouds. When he saw a beautiful cloud formation he would call his mother to come and see what he had painted in the sky. When he was old enough to mow the lawn, his parents became increasingly aware of his artistic bent, for no other lawn in Crawfordville exhibited designs of stars, birds, and animals.

Elberton photographer Everett Saggus was elected to the Royal Photographic Society of Great Britain in 1976.

At the age of ten, the world of photography opened up for this young boy when he won a Brownie camera by selling Ferry's seeds. When he was fourteen, Saggus used this camera to win first prize in a photography contest.

After his high school days and a course in commercial art, Saggus got a job as assistant artist at the Fox Theater in Atlanta. Carter Barron hired him with the stipulation that if the Fox made enough money during the week, the young fledgling would receive a ten dollar bill on Saturday night. Saggus lived with his brother, Oliver, who was one of the architects who helped design the Fox Theater. When the depression came, Oliver went back home to Crawfordville, and Everett Saggus recalls the days that followed:

"I remember the empty feeling I had when I went without food for two days and nights. The floor of the Fox was hard, but it was better than sleeping on the streets. At that time the Shriners had an office at the Fox, and when the Potentate heard about my plight, he unlocked a door in the theater and invited me into a beautifully furnished living area which included a bedroom and kitchen. He handed me the key and told me that I could stay there as long as the Fox remained open, and he was as good as his word."

When the Fox closed, Saggus returned to Crawfordville and worked with his father, Marshall Redmond Saggus, who was a merchant. After his marriage to Elizabeth Hill of Crawfordville, he opened two stores in Warrenton and Thomson, but photography remained his consuming interest. His living room became his studio, and his darkroom was in one of his stores.

After managing a studio in Columbia, South Carolina, for a short while, he moved to Elberton where he has lived and operated a studio for thirty-four years. He is quick to say that "the best folks in the world are right here in Elberton."

In reminiscing, the Elbertonian admits he cannot fulfill all requests. One man brought in a picture of a bird dog who was supposed to be pointing a covey of quail, but his tail was straight down. The customer said, "When you reprint this picture, be sure the dog's tail is straight out."

Weddings can provide near catastrophes. The photographer remembers one bride who was ready to walk down the aisle. When Saggus noticed something drooping below her train, he touched her arm and said, "Wait a minute. Something is wrong down there."

As she took a step, a white petticoat fell a little more below the train. The photographer said, "Start walking and I'll pull the slip off." With his help the beautiful bride obediently stepped out of the extra petticoat and walked on down the aisle.

Saggus' perceptive strength is revealed when he says these words: "I believe that at one time or another, everything that God creates is beautiful. It might be beautiful for one split second, and never again, but at one time it blossoms out in all its glory."

This master of photography believes in the youth of today, and he sees real achievement for those who will devote hard work and discipline to their chosen profession. These simple rules put into practice have brought scores of honors to Everett Saggus. He has won many state and international awards in contests and exhibits. As a member of the Professional Photographers of America he was the first Georgian to receive the National Award for "unselfish contribution to professional photography." He is a certified National Salon Judge and an Elector to the Hall of Fame of the Photographic Art and Science Foundation. He is past president of the Georgia Professional Photographers Association, and for eleven consecutive years he has been listed in *Who's Who in Photography*.

A great moment in his life came when the City of Elberton proclaimed *Everett Saggus Day*. One of his greatest triumphs was when Beta Sigma Phi Sorority sponsored him in a one-man exhibit at the Elberton Civic Center. It was an equally proud moment for his wife, his daughter and son-in-law, Peggy and Charles Van Pelt, and his two grandsons, Charlie and Jeffrey, of Roswell.

Will this man retire? The answer is no. "God and nature offer far too many miracles for me to think about quitting. I do not want to retire as long as I am physically and mentally able to move on."

1977

Author's note: Everett Saggus died on January 31, 1979. At the 1979 Founders Day Banquet, the Xi Alpha Rho Chapter of Beta Sigma Phi presented a "People Helping People Award" to his family in grateful memory of Saggus' service to his community and to Beta Sigma Phi.

Frank Wansley,
A Man of Many Talents

Elbert County owes a debt of gratitude to a native son who has brought to light the rich heritage of his own county and state. Frank Nicholas Wansley may not have amassed a fortune like Joseph Rucker, Georgia's first millionaire, but he has accumulated a wealth of historic material, and he has given it to the Elberton Historical Society. This collection is in the Frank Wansley Room at the Christmas Tree House. He is the author of *From Rome to Ruckersville—Our Wansley History* and can tell you whether to brag about your ancestors or just "lay low." His next book to be published is the *History of Vans Creek Baptist Church of Ruckersville*, said to be Georgia's oldest Baptist church in continuous service.

Frank Wansley uses a stethoscope to amplify the beat when balancing the tick and the tock of a clock pendulum.

Old-timers in Ruckersville say that Frank came into the world knowing how to make a clock run and how to play a violin. Of the thousands of clocks he has repaired and built, he prefers the old-fashioned pendulum clock. He looks like a doctor of horology as he uses a stethoscope to amplify the beat in order to get an exact balance between the tick and the tock. At present he is building a case for a clock with Westminster chimes, but he says he now does well just to take care of his regular "patients."

When he was barely able to hold a violin he played his first tune, *Little Brown Jug,* and he remembers the words: "Me and my wife and my little feist dog crossed the creek on a hickory log."

Listening to Fritz Kreisler playing Dvořák's *Humoresque* on a Brunswick phonograph, he succeeded in getting exactly the same sound and tone. When he played along with the record, listeners heard the sound of only one violin. He has been asked if his violin is a Stradivarius, but the country boy from Ruckersville admits he just has a plain old fiddle.

"I guess I've been the happiest country boy in the whole wide world," he says as he looks back on his seventy-seven years. "Strict discipline did not squelch my sisters, brothers, or me. It made us know that our mother and father loved us. Our father told us that if he ever heard of our stealing anything or telling a lie or not paying back some honest money that we owed, we wouldn't have to go to hell to see the devil. We'd see him in Ruckersville."

When Frank was a little boy he started whittling and made scrub boards that he sold for ten cents at his father's general store. They never locked the door when they went home to dinner. He recalls the happy memories of walking down a cedar lane with his father and the warmth he felt as he saw his mother standing in the doorway of a home that was never locked.

The woods and creeks furnished ample room for hunting, fishing and trapping. He became interested in taxidermy and picked enough cotton to pay $1.60 for a book on the subject. His father said, "Son, you could have bought a good pair of shoes for that." The subject of shoes did not come up again after Frank sold fur neckpieces and chokers to ladies all over Georgia.

Years ago when he built a little log cabin in Ruckersville, his father vowed that a cabin built with vertical logs would fall down after the first high wind. But the young man with a mind of his own had a different notion. He used one-inch rough boards at a 45-degree angle inside the logs. Through every board into each vertical log he drove two 20-penny nails. He

Everett Saggus

Although he doesn't know one note from another, Frank Wansley has been able to play the violin since early childhood.

ceiled the cabin with old-style beaded tongue-and-grooved pine boards. No log was more than five or six inches in diameter. The cabin did not collapse, and L. H. Wansley admitted that a vertically built log cabin had a mighty good chance of standing up under a Georgia tornado.

The man with many talents saw no reason to rush into matrimony, for, as he observed, "Cupid sometimes makes you act stupid." But when Ruby Moss, one of Elberton's most beloved nurses, came along, he asked her to marry him and live in his log cabin. She agreed, and Frank says that was the smartest thing he ever did. They lived there until 1944, when they moved into a home four miles from Elberton on Highway 368.

He was one of the first in Elbert County to buy a Model T Ford, and he became one of the first Model T mechanics in the county. He charged five dollars for overhauling a motor. During the depression he was swamped with repairing clocks, sewing machines, and Model T's. During that time he bought a walnut tree for one dollar and from it built a four-poster bed, a dresser, and a desk!

Frank Wansley wears many hats. Friends and neighbors call him "Mr. Resource Man." Others know him as the Cedar Post Tycoon, Mr. Sand Man, or as a surveyor. Part of his father's estate was a large number of cedar trees.

A manufacturer of cedar chests bought the trees on the stump. After they were cut, the tops and logs were left, and Frank bought them from the estate and began buying cedar trees from his neighbors. He has sold more than a million posts.

Years ago he went into partnership with Luther Burton to form the Coldwater Sand Operation, which has pumped many truckloads of sand each day for seventeen years.

Now, Frank Wansley builds birdhouses and feeders of cedar.

When he put one up on a Friday last July, a pair of bluebirds moved in on Monday. The new homemakers seemed to like their Swiss chalet with its little ornamental balcony of twigs and a perch under the door. He has been so deluged with orders he says he can only build for his own birds and friends.

He has especially enjoyed surveying, and proudly says that he has never been in a witness chair for an error. Because of his health he gave up this activity in 1976, but he has never stopped working, listening, studying, and answering the needs of others.

1980

Walter Jones, Rural Carrier

Take a few traits of a family doctor, some of a country minister, a trace or two of lawyer, a large portion of plain errand boy, an optimistic outlook, a strong back, a reasonably good mind, and a heart full of human kindness. Shake thoroughly every day over eighty miles of country roads, and you have a rural mail carrier.

Walter C. Jones, veteran carrier on Route 1, Dewey Rose, Georgia, and one of the oldest carriers in point of service in the United States, has long since ceased to be surprised at anything his patrons ask of him. After forty-three years of fulfilling unusual missions, a man acquires a pleasant indifference to buying baby pants, taking measurements for foundation garments, or buying youthforms for every conceivable figure, and he believes that he is probably entitled to a medal for extraordinary heroism in purchases for patrons.

His present route includes eighty miles of Elbert and Hart County roads, the weather largely determining their condition. He can be sure of either a smokescreen of dust or mile upon mile of almost impenetrable red mud. Dewey Rose, Georgia, nestled in the hills of Elbert County, is a typical northeast Georgia village consisting of two country stores and two filling stations, a church, a school, and a dozen or more homes surrounded by cotton and corn fields. In the horse and buggy days, the farmers in the adjoining territory were served by two rural routes, but improved roads and automobiles make it possible for one route to serve them now.

Although in mileage Mr. Jones has gone around the world more than twenty-four times, he still remembers the first morning he went to work. The fact that during the eighteen years of his life his visits to town had been very few did not make him feel too comfortable on that crisp September morning in 1902 when he entered the lamp-lit confusion of the post office, where three other rural carriers far older than he were casually sorting their mail for the day.

"I was clumsy and skittish as I shuffled those letters, but when I climbed into my road cart and started on my twenty-eight-mile route, my spirits revived and they were inclined to soar as I thought of the fifty dollars I was to receive every month just for taking letters to farm folks who couldn't go to town every day. I knew, however, by their reaction that my patrons were wondering why in creation Theodore Roosevelt should let that young sprout carry the mail and pay him two dollars a day for riding all over the country in a roadcart."

After eight years of using a horse and cart, the young carrier swapped the cart for a buggy. In the meantime he had become a master at breaking in any sort of horse or mule that his patrons had found too tough to handle. From earliest childhood he had spent much of his time in the wake of, or more often on the back of, every sort of farm animal from a bull calf to a spirited colt, and he always wound up by making friends with the animal. As a result, he didn't believe there was a horse or mule living that he couldn't tame, and some patron was always asking him to prove it.

They asked him to break everything from a Tennessee walking horse to a balking Georgia mule, and he never turned them down. It saved the energy of his own horses and gave him a lot of fun. But the going was not always utopian. There was the time when a horse he was breaking in became terrified by one of those newfangled contraptions that a fellow named Henry Ford had made and turned loose on the country. At the sight of the thing, the horse simply went away from there leaving Mr. Jones pinned under the buggy. An old farmer found him a little later, slightly bruised and stunned but still of the opinion that he could drive anything that walked on four legs.

Unbroken horses were not the only hazard on the road in those early days. Sometimes the weather went on a rampage and made the gentlest animal go to pieces. Lightning was the cause of more than one runaway, and one time the carrier had to lead his mare into a deep gully and talk soothingly to her while a violent windstorm roared overhead taking the tops off of trees all around.

Once when Mr. Jones was trying to ford a stream, the swift current turned the buggy over. The horse swam out, and so did the mail carrier—after he failed to grab the nearest limb. "That is the only time I ever lost any mail, and everything went down the stream except one registered letter. That letter turned out to be pretty important because the woman who received it decided she would give that no-count husband of hers another chance since he sent her a roll of bills."

"I was really prepared for winter in the horse-and-buggy days. When I rode in a cart in rainy weather, I carried a big umbrella, had a storm robe made of oilcloth, a lantern in the foot of the cart and either a hot brick or a jug of hot water for my feet. I wore long underwear, two pairs of pants, and two or three homespun wool shirts. My coonskin cap had flaps over the ears. But what helped more than all the riggings was the cup of steaming black coffee or bowl of hot soup that some kind friend on the route was sure to have waiting for me."

When the route was at its muddiest, and, as the saying goes, when

Walter C. Jones made his last round as rural carrier on March 31, 1954, after over fifty-one years of service. There were copies of the Elberton Star *in the first batch of mail he delivered, and a lot more were in the last.*

only fools and mail carriers were out, Mr. Jones rode horseback and his workday began long before sunrise and ended after dark. Those were the days to try any man's stamina with combinations of rain, sleet, and snow. They made him wonder if it wouldn't have been better to stick to farming after all. Those were the days that the mail carrier prayed for a complete absence of applications for money orders, those little time-takers that delay a man when he wants to get home out of the cold. And those were the days that his prayers bounced back and half the patrons wanted to order something from Sears, Roebuck.

For several years a motorcycle was his means of travel, and a few times he pedaled a bicycle. But only a few times, Mr. Jones hastens to admit.

"I was never fond of the bicycle, and I lost my yen for the motorcycle the day a hog crossed the road. I hit her, and, besides tearing up my britches, I woke up an hour later in a cotton patch. So I swapped the motorcycle for God's salvation to mail carriers, a Model T, and it is the only time I ever struck a bargain. The newer cars may have more gadgets, but the Model T didn't need them."

When Mr. Jones opens the mailbox he is never sure what he will find. It is not always a pound of country sausage or a bucket of Georgia sorghum. One day when he stopped at a box where the flag was up, he reached in to get the mail, and his hand jerked out just ahead of a snake who obviously didn't care to be disturbed. Behind some bushes nearby, a man guffawed his appreciation of the carrier's reaction. Another day he opened the same box and pulled out a hoot owl.

Knowledge of first aid should be on the list of requirements for a good mail carrier, according to Mr. Jones.

"In labor cases I feel mighty helpless; but I can go for the doctor. In prescribing for flu and pneumonia, I tell them what sunshine, eggs, and milk won't cure, God and mustard plaster will."

There was the time that a boy stuck a locust thorn completely through his foot, and the family begged the mailman to do something. The little fellow eyed him suspiciously from behind his mother's skirts when he saw a pair of pliers in the man's hand. But after he was told to close his eyes and count ten and promised that he could see the Saturday wild west show, he reluctantly obeyed. The amateur doctor yanked out the thorn and called for some turpentine to pour over the wound. Following the parents' expressions of gratitude and the stunned silence of the patient, Mr. Jones cranked up and drove leisurely on.

About five years ago, Mr. Jones exchanged his route with another rural carrier and left his then forty-four-mile route for the present one. Now with his long route that serves approximately three thousand people he retires by first dark and gets up between four-thirty and five o'clock, cooks his own breakfast, and during the winter months is delivering the mail before dawn.

The length of his route does not prevent him from stopping long enough to tell his friends that old Mr. Smith had a stroke, that Mrs. Johnson had twin boys, that the weather man says continued rain and not much change in temperature, and that the Germans and Japs can't last forever. They in turn advise him to slice an Irish potato in two and rub a piece of it on his bald head and he may have as good luck as did old man Brown, who now has a flourishing mop of hair. They tell him when to kill his pig and warn against planting unless the moon is just right. Judging from the tough pig meat he had last year and the series of crop failures of which the mail carrier has been a victim, he is inclined to believe that his farmer friends and Grier's Almanac may be right about this moon business after all.

To have a namesake, regardless of color or creed, is a constant source of joy to the veteran carrier. He can count scores of children who bear his name, many of whom are now in the armed forces. Recently he ran up on one of his name bearers, grown to manhood, who, in his youth, had fervently vowed that he would be a mail carrier like Mr. Jones. His apologies were profuse when he confessed that he had turned out to be a preacher.

Late in the afternoon when the carrier returns from his route, his extra duties begin. He gets out his shopping list, which may include a subscription to the local paper, women's dresses for such auspicious occasions as weddings and funerals, birthday and Christmas gifts, hats, medicines, groceries, children's toys, needles, pins, thread, patterns, tobacco, and snuff. For those whose trips to town are limited to once or twice a year, he cheerfully does their shopping, but he repeatedly warns the women that he will not be responsible for the similarity in design or color of hats, which invariably will be red.

The thoughtful things they do for Mr. Jones will never become an old story to him. He is frequently invited to "light and eat" country ham and red gravy, and during the summer he often stops at a farm house to fill up on watermelon and peaches. And the wells and springs go uncounted where he has stopped to drink and rest a moment from driving. He often returns home with gifts of fruit, vegetables, cake, honey, flowers, fruit trees. In fact they will give him almost everything but their sugar stamp.

In spite of some highly tense moments, he has never witnessed a killing, an excellent record considering all the arguments he has been asked to help settle and the fights he has been called on to referee. After silently watching the feathers fly, Mr. Jones drives off with the parting reminder that none of us have sprouted wings. He recollects with pride that he has been instrumental in numerous married couples patching up their differences and making another try at staying together and usually succeeding. He often tells the story of what he terms one of his greatest triumphs. Years ago a friend on his route quit his wife and vowed he was through forever. He would have been if it had not been for the persistent pleas of the mail carrier over a period of eight years. Finally the man's stern resolve crumbled.

"Mr. Jones," he said, "I'm goin' back to that old crab but this ain't my doin'. Now, remember, if she's hell to live with this time, she's yours." Luckily, Mr. Jones observes, they are still scrapping, more or less, together.

War has its advantages in keeping a man and wife together, he believes. One woman who admitted that she didn't love her soldier husband said the monthly allotment check kept her from getting a divorce. She was not so happy when she was later notified that her husband was being discharged from the army.

The days that he delivers a message telling of a son missing or killed in action are the hard ones. Nothing is more moving than the stony gaze of a mother as she reads the notice from the war department. Recently a woman became hysterical over something less serious, a mirror broken in shipping.

"I've been wondering," he laughed, "if her tears came from sentiment or if she was afraid of seven years of bad luck."

Another time a woman started yelling and screaming and calling on the Lord for assistance when she was handed a special delivery letter. The mail carrier tried to tell her it might be good news. Upon opening it, she resumed her unbridled cries to high heaven. The letter told her that ten relatives were coming to visit her soon.

Old and young greet the mailman on his daily rounds, for in out-of-the-way places, the coming of the mail is the most important event of the day. This is especially true with expectations of servicemen's letters and allotment and alimony checks. They meet him in everything from diapers to overalls and from shorts to housecoats. The feeble and the sprightly, the lame and the blind, the mothers with babies at their breasts. Not only children but grown folks wait hours to be the first to get the mail.

The fact that he may have a double-barrel shotgun on the back seat of his car does not afford his friends any alarm, for they have long since learned that their mail carrier is looking out for game and they know that the little tin bucket in his car means that he's going to stop for fish bait at some minnow-rich stream. His favorite recreation is fishing, and great is his joy in landing a big fish. "When I retire," he says, "I want to go where the fishing's good."

Throughout the years Mr. Jones has never remembered a completely uneventful trip. Ordinary bees and wasps have afforded much uncomfortable commotion, and buzzards flying low have made it difficult to stay in the road. On many occasions the brakes have given way and coming home unscarred has been an admixture of the driver's prowess and God's goodness. When asked if his car has ever turned over he admits that it has "tilted" a time or two.

Besides the word *fish, fair and warmer* are the most beautiful words Webster ever ran across, from the mail carrier's point of view. The words that are not exactly thrilling are *box holders, catalogs,* and *chain letters.*

As a whole he has found his many patrons exceptionally honest. On occasion, there are some who want to mail letters and packages and who are completely without any money. They do not hesitate to give Mr. Jones everything from quail to goat to get their things mailed.

Several years ago the mailman drove up to his home and noiselessly walked in. His mouse-like approach was caused by his absence of shoes. To the inquiries made by his family he merely remarked, "I found a man who needed them more than I did."

His job is rich in dividends. Regardless of the heavy mail and the long route, he stops and cuts off the motor at the top of a long hill and scans the rolling country. He takes time to pick a few blackberries or take home a bit of pink honeysuckle and laurel or a handful of violets. Wildlife is plentiful along the forest roads. He often encounters red foxes, squirrels, rabbits, and possums. One morning long before day, he caught a possum that was nonchalantly ambling across the road. "It was just a question of outwalking the possum," he says.

A real satisfaction comes from being one of thirty-three thousand rural mail carriers who, all told, travel more than one million miles to serve more

It has been said that love and time with reverence use. It's a good way to live.
—Lois Jones

than twenty-nine million people daily, and "neither snow, nor rain, nor gloom of night shall stay them.'

The rewards are many for the mailman who stops daily to read the headlines and tell the latest news to a blind old man who waits patiently for his arrival, or to stop and write a letter for one who never learned to write, or to try to explain just why young John had to die across the sea away from everybody who loved him.

There's no explaining the sense of absolute peace that comes from seeing a green pasture full of white-faced cows laconically munching grass, or waving to an old lady rocking on her porch and puffing contentedly on her corncob pipe. There's no grander feeling than having the love and good will of scores of people and the grateful appreciation of some friend who mumbles, "God bless you, Mr. Jones."

"I love my route and the thousands that I have served. If I could live another lifetime I would serve thousands more.

"There's a young high school boy who stays out of school on rainy days so he can go with me and help me out of the ditch if I get in one," Mr. Jones says. "I suppose I shall want to carry the mail as long as boys want to play hooky from school to ride with me."

1945

Sister Gertrude's Charlotte

Who has inspired me? My Aunt Ellen Bradley. In her home town of Sandersville and all over Washington County she is known as "Miss Ellen." Her teaching career as a first-grade teacher spanned many years, and when she had to retire officially, she kept on doing substitute teaching in whatever grade was needed. One of her crowning achievements was to create better relations when racial tensions were high.

One of her great loves has always been the Transylvania Club, a literary club in Sandersville. Members of this organization have had many bake sales to raise money to build a library and support other projects.

My aunt has a famous recipe, Sister Gertrude's Charlotte, and as long as she was able, she stayed busy filling orders for this delectable dessert. She insists that her directions be followed to the letter.

Sister Gertrude's Charlotte
1 pint whipping cream
4 egg whites
1 cup sweet milk
1½ tablespoons Knox gelatin
1 scant cup sugar
2 teaspoons vanilla or 2½ tablespoons sherry

1. Soak gelatin in milk.
2. Whip cream slightly stiff. Put aside.
3. Whip egg whites until they stand in peaks, add sugar, whip, put aside. (Cream and eggs may be whipped with a portable electric mixer.)
4. Dissolve gelatin over hot water (not boiling), stirring constantly, cool. Over cold water continue to stir. Use hand eggbeater and pour gelatin slowly into egg white, add flavoring.

5. Whip this mixture into cream with hand beater. Pour into mold which has been rinsed with cold water and not dried. Refrigerate. Can top with fruits when serving. Makes 12 servings.

—Dorothy Hardy Fortson

Mr. Charlie

If the art of mankind is to polish the world and if everyone who works is scrubbing in some part, then eighty-four-year-old Charles Witcher Faust of Lexington has done his share of polishing on his home place, one of the oldest plantations in Georgia. Don't expect to find Mr. Charlie dozing in a rocking chair. He's more likely to be found on a tractor plowing up new ground or cutting up cords of wood for winter warmth.

The Faust plantation, a land grant dating back to the 1780s, has been home to seven generations of the Faust family. In 1810 Mr. Charlie's great-grandparents, John Phillip Faust and Christina Faust, moved from South Carolina to Georgia and lived in a two-room log cabin near Indian Creek in Oglethorpe County, about seven miles from Lexington. The original cabin, now used as a dining room and kitchen, is joined by a covered passageway from the back porch to the newer house built in 1890.

The large dining room has walls of exposed logs, twelve inches square and hand-planed to a smooth finish. The logs are chinked with beveled boards, and the exposed beams of the ceiling support the upper floor. Board-and-batten doors are hung with strap hinges.

The smoke house, blacksmith shop, and tenant houses have disappeared, but the buggy house, supply house, and the first cotton gin in Oglethorpe County still remain. The gin is an exact model of the one designed by Eli Whitney. The farmers would take their bales of cotton to Augusta in wagons pulled by oxen and bring back yearly supplies.

Mr. Charlie now lives alone in the old home at the end of Faust Road. His wife, the former Louellen Landers of Decatur, Alabama, died sixteen years ago. Sometimes loneliness crowds in too close, but he is thankful for his three children and their families. Two of his children, Mrs. Walter Mathews and James Faust, live nearby. His older son Howard lives in Warner Robins. If picking up an ax and splitting wood won't ward off lonely days, his grandchildren and great-grandchildren will!

For many years, Mr. Charlie has been an active member of Bethany Baptist Church, formerly called Indian Springs Church. He has served as deacon, clerk, treasurer, and teacher, but as for preaching he left that job to his brother Will. The late William H. Faust, noted state evangelist, organized the Gordon Street Baptist Church in Atlanta.

The fields of cotton on the Faust plantation have long since gone. In their place are thousands of chickens and fenced-in pasture land where cattle graze. Many things will be remembered about this old home: the banisters that happy children slid down; the old oak bed in which Mr. Charlie was born and where he has no trouble in falling asleep; the beautiful quilts made by his great-grandmother's children; a bookcase filled with rare old volumes; and Gina, who calls her grandfather to supper as dusk gentles into the folds of night.

Everett Saggus

Mr. Charlie Faust grew up in the home that had been in his family for seven generations. The original log cabin is now used as a dining room and kitchen. A covered passageway connects the cabin to the newer house built in 1890.

But most of all, the man at the end of the old Faust Road will be the one you won't forget—a man whose life shows that wealth is not measured by clink of coins.

1977

William B. Winburn

Fair-owner I. V. Hulme believes that "when you get sawdust in your shoes, you can never shake it out."

I. V. Hulme: "Mister Fairman"

"When you get sawdust in your shoes, you can never shake it out," says I.V. Hulme. And who should know that better than this gentleman from Elberton, who has managed hundreds of fairs and owned many of them.

In 1936, during his first three attempts at operating fairs in Elberton, Gainesville, and Winder, heavy rains fell on fifteen of the eighteen operating days of his fairs. If three failures in a row won't change a man's mind about a lifetime career, then rain won't *rain* him out. Again in 1954 it rained a solid week in Elberton, and he did not take in a dime. He advised his hometown friends: "If anybody's got turnips to plant, they should get 'em ready for it'll rain for sure."

For many years I.V. has studied all the almanacs, the long weather forecasts and his horoscope, and he has come up with a few observations— there is no such thing as a foolproof almanac and the same can be said for weather predictions. Astrological study may bolster morale but Pisces won't pay bills. Just plain hard work is the only answer, according to I.V. Hulme.

"I never did know anything but work," he says. "I never went fishing and I never got to play ball but I didn't resent it. I just made up my mind to be happy and that's the way I have been all my life. In business I get mad but I forget it. I get mighty put out about something but I never hold a grudge. A grudge is a deep, deadly poison. When I was eight years old I worked on signs for my father, Thomas Jefferson Hulme, who owned an outdoor advertising company in Elberton. The only hobby I had was to go to every circus I could find.

"I guess the fair bug bit me when I was born. When I was a teenager I placed signs in the Southeastern Fair in Atlanta. Free passes came with the signs, which went up on telephone poles and the sides of barns. I took a pup tent to Atlanta and camped out during the week of the fair."

Show business is just naturally in his blood. He played the saxophone in Elberton High School and at Mercer University and formed his own band, known in the twenties and thirties as Hulme's Seven Aces. That was his first business venture, and his band performed all over Georgia and the southeastern states.

"I attribute much of my success to the late J.A. Mitchell, one of the finest men who ever lived. When Mr. Mitchell was appointed head of the Virginia State Fair, I took his place as general manager of the Anderson Fair. I remember 1926 and a high wind that blew me some good. Mr. Mitchell was in Elberton trying to put up posters for the Anderson Fair. The wind was blowing so hard he couldn't get a poster up. I happened to be walking along at the right time and I gave him a hand. He paid me five dollars a day, and in those days that was big money."

He recalls the many times he placed fair signs at night by the light from a truck so he could be at the fair during the day. He slept from two to four hours on the office floor so he could be ready to help Mr. Mitchell the next day.

"And the day I married Idele Haley of Elberton, I knew Pisces was the right sign to be born under. My wife helps me in every living moment with all my plans and all my commitments."

The Hulmes can in no way forget the depression. "I used to paint signs all night long," said I.V. "I'd go to bed at four and get up at six and strike out and put them up all day."

"I can't forget it either," says Idele. "For twenty-two years we did not own a house. In the 1930s we paid five dollars a month for rent. I went to work and made thirteen dollars a week. I.V. worked at a grocery store and made a dollar and a half a day. We limited ourselves to one Coca-Cola a week. A telephone was out of the question."

Well, they are home owners now with a spacious home in Elberton, and an equally beautiful lakeside home. They have plenty of space for their hobbies. Idele collects Royal Bayreuth china and, besides I. V.'s initial circus hobby, he now collects coins, antique bottles, and paintings that include clocks that actually tick away the time.

I.V. admits that his greatest ambition in life has been to own a circus. "And," smiles his wife, "the best thing is that my husband has not fulfilled that particular ambition." Yet today, regardless of the fickle elements of nature, I.V. Hulme is a living symbol that rains at fair time cannot trounce a man permanently down.

His name is a byword in Florida, Georgia, and the Carolinas, where he is known for his artistic creations in advertising. He employs a staff of about thirty artists and servicemen and handles all types of advertising. He has a plant in Ocala, Florida, and maintains another in Anderson, South Carolina, but his headquarters and main facilities are in Elberton, his hometown. His advertising extends into Alabama, Tennessee, Kentucky, and Indiana.

Jim McHugh, a feature writer for *Amusement Business* had this to say about I.V.: "There are very few fairmen who know more show people than I.V. He has cultivated their friendship from the start and wherever the clan meets, including the winter festivals at New York and Chicago, he can be found. Throughout the year he receives dozens of calls from agents and managers wanting dates. He visits a great many fairs. His part of the country is pretty well dotted with annuals and he visits them all in the belief that one worthwhile idea picked up will justify the hefty schedule. I. V. believes that in the South a good livestock show and good school exhibits are necessary."

Mainly, I.V. wants his country fairs to remind folks of the good old days when everybody displayed something—an art or craft, a culinary perfection, flower or flower arrangement, a school exhibit, an animal or fowl, an industrial achievement, or photography.

I.V. likes to work under pressure. During the fair season he averages only a few hours sleep at night. "The bigger the pressure, the better I feel," he says. A real showman, he will be dressed in colorful attire. He will be found watching the 4-H and FFA cattle owners operating their private beauty shop to get their prize cows ready for the show with hair trimmed and brushed until it glows and shines. He will be served cotton candy by beautiful girls and will sample a lemon pie. He may be found admiring a crocheted bedspread with a design as intricate as a "fairy web that catches and holds the dew of morning."

For the midway he believes in performances that will give everybody a lot of fun and leave a good memory—spectacular acts, the best circus performances, and celebrities such as Tex Ritter, Jo Anne Castle, Loretta Lynn, and many other famous people. I.V. has a particular yen for country music and gospel singing.

He may not own a circus, but oh, how the people and the excitement get to him when summer slips away into the folds of autumn and it's fair time once again. The ceremony of the cutting of the ribbons . . . a mother holding a baby in her arms and a toddler by her side . . . children and teenagers rushing in . . . an old man hobbling with a cane . . . hot dogs and onions . . . hamburgers . . . sawdust under foot . . . nostalgia of high school graduates reluctant to go to college and miss the fair for the very first time.

I.V. is a joiner. He is a member of the Moose, Elks, Redmen, WOW, Showmen's League of America, and National Showmen's Association. He is also a member of the Outdoor Association of America and is a director of the Georgia Outdoor Association and a former president of the Georgia Association of Agricultural Fairs. He is a member of the Yaarab Temple of the Shrine in Atlanta, and in his hometown of Elberton, he is active in the Chamber of Commerce, the country club, the Elk's Lodge, and is a loyal member of the First Baptist Church. His loyalty to his church started as early as he could lift a saxophone, for he and his brother Joseph played for the Sunday School Assembly when they were quite young.

I.V. Hulme believes in the young folks of today and this is the advice he offers them: "Live on bread and water until you get a foothold. Do the best you can and live a good life. It's simple enough. Just live by the Golden Rule."

1974

Claude Stevens, Master Carver and Artist

In the village of Carlton in Madison County lives a master wood-carver whose lifelong dream has been to create something of beauty. And from the evidence of his skill and craftsmanship, Claude Stevens' dream has come true.

After a life as soldier, teacher, surveyor, naturalist, historian, and author, he is convinced that his best decision was made on the day he picked up a pocketknife when he was quite young and started whittling. Since his retirement from teaching physics and mathematics, he has devoted long hours each day and night to carving and wood sculpture.

The wood-carver and his wife, the former Lois Thornton, are native

Everett Saggus

Master carver Claude Stevens expresses his artistic vision through the medium of wood-carving.

Georgians, and live in the beautiful old home where Mr. Stevens was born. His display of carvings in their home includes Georgia's state bird, the brown thrasher, and a kinglet, bluebird, blue jay, yellow-shafted flicker, tufted titmouse, cardinal, and chickadee. A robin pulls a worm from the ground. A miniature red-winged blackbird flies into cattail rushes; close by are Mama Quail and her three babies and a miniature hen and five baby chicks. They are all carved to precise scale.

His art forms go far beyond the aviary. His subjects come from the Bible, mythology, history, fiction, fable, sports, and nursery rhymes. One of his largest carvings, fashioned from a single block of holly, is a replica of Michelangelo's statue of Moses. One of his smallest is a butterfly on a flower stalk mounted on a date seed.

Carved figures include David with his sling, the graceful goddess Diana, Alice in Wonderland, Long John Silver, Jim Hawkins, Ichabod Crane, and Old King Cole and his Fiddlers Three.

Carvings of the madonna and child, kissing angels and the bringing in of the yule log give a feeling that Christmas is not far away. There is a holiday table with a tray of miniature dishes. Nine Chippendale chairs carved from balsa wood are placed around the table. A butler brings in the plum pudding on a tray decorated with holly. Three tiny figures are ready to enter the little

Everett Saggus

This peacock carved by Claude Stevens stands less than four inches tall.

This madonna and child are carved of holly wood.

church with a steeple. Within the church they will find a miniature pulpit carved out of unpainted pine.

The sculptor's ingenuity is a constant surprise. For instance, the figure of a girl and boy dancing is fashioned from a plum pit. Male and female bobwhites are carved from the meats of two chestnuts. A minute jar was once an olive pit, a cherry pit is transformed into a seated figure on the edge of a tub, and from a hickory nut emerge two checker players with one of the players scratching his head, perhaps to mull over his next move.

In his *Self-portrait,* Claude Stevens depicts himself as a surveyor sighting through his transit. For this carving he selected holly, his favorite wood.

Today his workshop has many more tools than a pocketknife. He uses detachable wood-carving blades, chisels, mallets, handsaws, coping saws, and dental drills. It does not disturb him if someone watches as he carves, but he feels he must be alone when using a handsaw or a power tool.

For a while the wood-carver sold some of his carvings, but he found that selling diminished the joy of creating something of beauty. Through gifts, however, to many relatives and friends and from earlier sales, his objets d'art are found throughout the United States and a number of foreign countries.

He has exhibited wood sculptures and carvings at the University of Georgia Museum of Art in Athens and in Georgia libraries. He has given woodcarvings of Uncle Remus, Br'er Rabbit, Br'er Fox, Br'er Coon, and Tar Baby to the Joel Chandler Harris Museum in Eatonton.

Claude Stevens is truly a master craftsman with an artistic talent for transforming pieces of wood into carvings of amazing beauty.

1977

Herbert Wilcox, the Georgia Scribe

When Herbert Wilcox left the old Wilcox Pasture in Elberton for a greener one, someone said that time may bring us here and time may take us away but Mr. Herbert will always be around.

His friends remember him walking down McIntosh Street to the home where he was born or typing away in the *Elberton Star* office. From his many published articles emerged a classic book, *Georgia Scribe,* carefully compiled by his wife, Irene Stilwell Wilcox. He captured Georgia's past and gently, with humor and pathos, linked yesterday with today.

What he wrote just seemed to spill out like the tumbling water of Broad River. Folks chuckled as he reminded them of the days "when small boys wore knee pants and men wore long britches, and both wore shirts, with tails tucked in, when in public."

Once when Mr. Wilcox and his daughter Martha were walking down a winding path in the Wilcox pasture, she asked who made the pasture. He told her God made it. "God is a good sport," she said.

Deep in the winter woods he could kneel down and gently uncover the magic of big blue violets blooming in December. Whatever the season, he

Elberton's Herbert Wilcox was known and loved as a writer and philosopher.

found little bits of wonder—bluets, trillium, hepatica, mosses, and ferns tipped by magic wands.

The young and the old know the way to the Wilcox door. In search of many things—woods gardens, history, genealogy, security, or the comfort of the rocking chairs in the family room. A child recently came and asked if she could dust the little log cabin that Mr. Wilcox had built and furnished with minute carvings and just plain whittling.

Folks agree with the man who said that nobody is going to have a better time in heaven than Mr. Herbert. He will no doubt make a thorough investigation of celestial quarters and will continue to uncover the little bits of wonder. Maybe with a microscope.

1977

Mr. Mell and His Indian Relics

After serving as principal in the schools of Georgia for fifty-one years, a man has the right to collect Indian relics as a hobby.

So thinks E. B. Mell of Athens, Georgia, who today has one of the finest arrowhead collections in the country.

Years ago he happened upon three arrowheads lying together, and his collecting began. Now he has more than sixty thousand arrows that are classified according to type of rock, a miscellaneous group, and thousands that are not yet grouped. Besides these, he has countless drills, scrapes, and arrowheads.

Mr. Mell prefers to go alone on his jaunts. The walking stick that he carries does not mean that he is trying to look dapper and impress the ladies, nor does it mean that he is suffering from old-fashioned rheumatism, for the collector depends greatly upon his dogwood stick to unearth his findings.

Some time ago, while walking near the river at Athens, he saw in the red clay a black spot that seemed to be a fragment of pottery. After putting his familiar stick to use, he found the bottom of a bowl. Upon further investigation the bowl turned out to be a man's skull. Mr. Mell's hunting is mostly confined to cultivated fields, and although he has been offered the privilege of going into mounds, he refuses to dig in these burial places.

If the shades of the Indians who have already registered in their happy hunting ground could return and behold five hundred powerful tomahawks and a table of battle axes and arrowheads more than one thousand years old, all found by Mr. Mell, they would probably let out a mighty war whoop. Their mouths would water at the sight of the corn mills with which their energetic squaws ground corn, and at the cooking vessels in which they prepared food. Their hands would itch on beholding a variety of game rocks, and they would long to bowl again with the perfectly round disk-shaped stones, ranging from 1¼ inches in diameter to 5¼ inches.

But the returned braves would get their greatest satisfaction upon spying the perfect specimen of peace pipe, with the memories of pleasant moments of folded hands and retrospection that it would arouse.

Mr. Mell could set up an Indian relic shop of his own. He has a rock that looks like an owl, another shaped like a crow's head, one like a horse's head, and a part of a pipe that would easily pass for Donald Duck. A comb made of walnut is one of his prized possessions, and another of his favorites is an old flintlock that he found at Tugalo mound and that he believes belonged to DeSoto. Of unusual beauty is a water bottle made of orange and blue clay and having four medallions.

Although Mr. Mell has been a Sunday School superintendent for many years, he can nevertheless vie with any fisherman in spinning unlikely yarns. He recalls the day he was walking just out of Crawford, and picked up a piece of lip-shaped bowl. Fifteen months later, walking over the same property, he found the other three sides to the bowl. The pieces fitted perfectly. The only missing bit was a tiny part of the bottom, and he hopes to find that some day.

Another far-fetched tale resulted from a stroll Mr. Mell took along the Apalachee River. He picked up a part of an Indian pipe of blue clay. A year later as he retraced his steps, his keen eye and prodding stick unearthed the other part of the pipe. And inside the pipe there still remained some unburned tobacco. Mr. Mell does not know how old the pipe is, but he does know that Indians left that region in 1838.

Some time ago, while strolling on the old William H. Crawford place, Mr. Mell saw what he thought was a leaf. As he kept pulling, the dainty leaf turned out to be a scalping knife 5¾ inches long, a beautiful specimen of olive green flint. Another specimen of more fearful proportions, 10¾ inches long, was unearthed on Jacob's Creek in Walton County.

Several years ago a soldier came and tried to buy the collection outright and even offered to mortgage his property for it, but went away convinced that money could not buy Mr. Mell's treasures. The soldier, however, went away with enough arrowheads to build a chimney.

1951

Author's note: Mr. Mell's collection of Indian relics is now at the anthropology department of the University of Georgia in Athens.

Thad Stevens, the Country Vet

Thad Stevens was the mayor of Carlton for many years and the best country veterinarian in Madison County. Money did not flow freely into his pocket, but he did receive special payments when he ministered to the needs of dogs, cats, cows, horses, and mules. Sometimes he received grits, turnips, collards, possum, and on a rare occasion, a whole ham. Twelve ears of corn if a cow got better, twenty-four if she totally recovered. Once when an ailing mule got well, Mr. Thad's wife received a crocheted afghan to meet the winter winds sifting through the windows.

The country vet never sent a bill to anyone. Why should he? If you helped a fellow, that was good pay.

One night when he was warm and safe in bed the telephone rang at eleven o'clock. A farmer who loved his cow was on the other end of the line. "I need you, Mr. Thad. if you don't come, my best Guernsey will die before daybreak."

Thad Stevens, full of sleep and the warmth of a hot jug at the end of

A hand-me-down piece of advice obtained from an old country store owner has given me a lot of smiles and miles. When asked how he managed to stay in business for so long and continue to make money he replied: "Son, I always work

his toes said, "John, it's fifteen miles to your farm. It's raining and it's supposed to snow, but meet me at the gate. My old car has been acting up lately. I won't promise for full but I'll try."

His wife protested, "Thad, please don't go out on a night like this! Your car won't crank half the time and you're too old for all this night life."

Rain, snow, and age didn't keep Mr. Thad from going out into the night. After stubborning six or seven times, his old jalopy cranked. He skidded down the road, hit more icy mud puddles than a fellow can talk about, and finally came to the gate. John Ellis was waiting at the gate, and he held up the barbed-wire fence so Mr. Thad could crawl under. By lantern light they walked a mile to the barn.

The country vet talked gently to Maude the Guernsey and he rubbed her soft-like.

"Maude," he said, "I have a little something that may hurt you for a minute, but after that you are going to be all right. Will you trust me?"

Sure she trusted him, just like everybody did. Maude laid her head on Thad Stevens' knee and closed her eyes. The needle was sharp and quick. After a while he cranked up his car and went on back to Carlton.

Several weeks later Mayor Thad and his cronies were gathered around a potbellied stove at Stevens-Martin Store, better known as Steve-Martin's. He was in the middle of telling one of his favorite yarns when John Ellis walked in. When the story ended, John took out a sizable roll of bills. "Mr. Thad, I owe you some money and I have come to pay my debt. Praise be to you, my Guernsey is giving enough milk for Madison County."

The country vet took his feet off the stove, got out a little old-fashioned computer of his own and made some notes. Then he said, "John, it's like this. You called me at 11 P.M. I was asleep. The night was cold and rainy and the dirt road was slick. It was fifteen miles to your farm. I had to stop my car at the gate, crawl under a barbed-wire fence and walk a mile to your barn. I gave your cow a shot and I stayed with her until she perked up. I finally made it back to the barbed-wire fence and got in my car. At four in the morning I crawled back into bed."

"I'm mighty grateful to you, Mr. Thad. Now how much does that come to?" asked the farmer.

Mr. Thad tilted his eyes upward. "John, considering everything, I guess that will be about fifty cents."

1984

on a one percent markup."

I asked how that would be successful.

"Son, I buys something for one dollar and I sells it for two dollars. That is one percent."

Need I say more?

—Ralph Chapman

One Thing Led to Another for Ann E. Lewis

Founder of *Georgia Magazine* and *Georgia Life*

Mrs. Ann E. Lewis, owner, editor, and manager of *Georgia Magazine*, was named writer of the month at the November 1961 dinner meeting of the Atlanta Writers' Club.

"I watched my mother write Bible story books but I never thought about writing until I married a man who did write," she said. Her husband,

In 1939 Ann Lewis traveled to the World's Fair in New York with her five children. The children are, left to right, Kitty, 9; Libby, 7; Robert, 6; and Ann, 10; with Billy, 12, standing behind and above the others.

William W. Lewis, is advertising director for a stock chain and is well known for his terse verse.

People in Whitmire, South Carolina, her home town, were without a newspaper, so they put the problem right in Mrs. Lewis' lap. At their insistence Mrs. Lewis agreed to start a newspaper. Hence the *Whitmire News*. She became country correspondent for the *Greenville News*, the *Spartanburg Herald* and the *Columbia Record*. She also wrote feature articles for these papers and for the *South Carolina Magazine*.

"My biggest thrill was when the *Greenville News* gave me a by-line on the front page. But my first big story was written about William Randolph Hearst's grandmother, who was born in Whitmire. It took me two years to run down the story, King Features bought it." As a result of this article, a friendship grew between her and Ethel Whitmire, cousin of Mr. Hearst. When Miss Whitmire invited Ann Lewis and her five children to be her guests in California, Ann couldn't think of any reason to keep her from going—except money for gas.

She called the managing editor of the *Greenville News* and asked him if he would pay her for a series of features on the California trip. At that time her children were four, five, seven, eight, and ten. His answer was leveled straight: "If you're fool enough to go to California, I'm fool enough to pay you." Two other newspaper editors followed suit. So Mrs. Lewis gained the name of being "that woman who went to California with all those children."

Several years later she took her children to the World's Fair in New York and paid for her trip by selling her travel stories to seven newspapers, including the *New York Herald Tribune*.

For ten years Mrs. Lewis dropped out of the writing field because of the duties of caring for an invalid aunt. After the death of her aunt in 1949, she resumed the publication of the *Whitmire News*.

In 1952 she moved to Decatur. It was a big change from a large home to apartment living. So for lack of elbow room and acres, the *Georgia Magazine* was born.

"I needed it and Georgia needed it, for I keenly felt that Georgia had a voice to be heard." At present 262 Georgia authors have been heard through the medium of her magazine. Georgia Magazine has reached a distribution point of 10,000 copies.

"I have six hobbies," Mrs. Lewis announced. "And all of them are grandchildren." And she frankly admits that she has two vices—collecting antiques and Dresden china.

1961

Elberton's Miss Emmie

Nancy Hart and Old Dan Tucker livened up Elbert County in the past, and Amelie de Launay Thompson adds spirit to the present. Mrs. Thompson, better known to Elbertonians as Miss Emmie, widow of the late Dr. D. N. Thompson, believes that with God and exercise you can do anything you make up your mind to do. Her proof seems ample. In the 1950s, after five operations as a result of a broken hip, orthopedic surgeons said that she would never walk again. Today at ninety-two, she not only walks, she sprints. Recently when she took an eye test to renew her driver's license, she was asked if she wore glasses. "Yes, when I read fine print," she replied. Miss Emmie's license was renewed.

Every morning after she checks on the needs of neighbors who are considerably younger but not nearly so spry, she works in her garden, prunes shrubbery, and chops wood. She agrees with Gladstone that chopping wood is an accomplishment and that it does wonders for the liver. Her flowers are her friends, and she talks to them. "They hear and solve my problems," she says, "and my anxieties are buried around my plants."

On her ninetieth birthday her children and grandchildren gave a tea in her honor and just about everybody in Elbert County came. It was a good time for Miss Emmie's former pupils to reminisce and exchange stories about their favorite teacher. For twenty-two years she had a School of Business Administration that might have been called a Business School of Life, for the subjects she taught went far beyond typing, shorthand, bookkeeping, ethics, commercial law, English, and spelling.

The school day started with meditation and a prayer of thanks just for being alive. A time to discover the beauty of the Bible . . ."the voice out of the whirlwind . . . when the morning stars sang together, and all the sons of God shouted for joy." Her class provided an exchange of ideas, and her "children" began to understand themselves and to become acquainted with philosophy, history, mythology, the great classics, and far-off places.

In both day and night classes, teenagers and oldagers followed Miss Emmie's limbering up exercises. They learned how to walk, talk, breathe, strengthen their eyes, bathe babies, and how to hold or lose a mate. Many students remembered the mischievous twinkle in their teacher's eyes when she said, "Never marry a man until you have investigated his insurance policy and until you have seen him in a bathing suit."

Carolyn Cann

Elberton's Miss Emmie celebrated her one-hundredth birthday on June 29, 1986. Miss Emmie says of herself that she has "the gift of never realizing there is a generation gap between young people and me."

A short time after starting on my first job, in a conversation with an older, successful man, he said to me, "Always remember that no business is any better than the service that goes with it."
Then a very prominent businessman who had withstood the cotton market crash in the early twenties by selling out a few days before the break in the

Staying in after school was pure pleasure. It provided a time to explore mathematics, gardening, air layering, plant propagation, and the stock market. If a group asked for lessons in ballet, ballroom dancing, horseback riding, or swimming, their requests were happily granted.

Naturally, the inimitable Miss Emmie had no problem with absenteeism. Her students were too eager to see what she was going to do next. They captured her enthusiasm for astronomy and astrology, and sometimes she obligingly rescheduled a test for those whose signs were unfavorable. When they begged her to tell the story of the Bell Witch in Tennessee or to tell about her opportunity to appear in a Broadway play, Miss Emmie knew beyond doubt that her class was unprepared for a test.

When she retired from teaching in 1945, she received gifts of jewelry, silver, and bonds, but she especially remembers her favorite gift that a class gave her one Christmas—a push plow for her rose garden, and she often laughs and says, "I was the mule who pushed the plow."

A number of years ago a patient walked into Dr. Thompson's office and said, "Doc, do you know what your wife is doing right now?" Dr. Thompson said there was no way to predict what "Emmie de" was going to do next.

"Well, sir, come with me." The doctor went to the window and saw his unpredictable wife perched precariously high in a pecan tree. She was knocking off pecans with one hand and holding onto a limb with the other. When "Emmie de" made her downward descent, her husband said, "Sweetheart, since our marriage I have never had one dull moment."

Miss Emmie's love for climbing trees began in her childhood days in Clarksville, Tennessee. When she was five, she climbed to the top limb of an apple tree. The limb broke and she fell to a lower limb. "I hung by my drawers for half an hour before I was rescued. Fortunately my mother always sewed an extra piece in the crotch. I was thankful for my mother's reinforcement."

A short time ago the nonagenarian was asked if she still climbed trees. "Yes," she said, "and I intend to keep on climbing as long as there is a tree to climb."

The beloved Elbertonian finds life too exciting to waste a moment. Several months ago *Iole*, her first book of historical fiction, was published, and she was honored at an autograph party at the Elbert County Library. At present she has four novels and three books of poems ready for publication. Her study bulges with Bibles, books, dictionaries, encyclopedias, magazines, newspapers, and mementos of her world travels. Miss Emmie's calendar is filled with dates for lectures at civic clubs, and because of her reputation as a Bible scholar, she is often invited to speak at churches in Elberton and neighboring towns.

If someone needs to find an answer, or if a problem towers too high, a solution may come from Miss Emmie. She unravels many tangled lives. She knows that she is psychic and she is aware of the power of ESP. She is grateful for her God-given memory. "The more you exercise your mind," she says, "the more it encompasses." And Kitten Cat, a nine-year-old Persian, purrs contentedly as she listens to her longtime friend.

Although Miss Emmie was born in Clarksville, Tennessee, her roots lie deep in Georgia. Her mother, Nina de Launay Nisbet, was the daughter of Amelie Mildred de Launay and Joseph Henry Nisbet of Milledgeville. He was owner and editor of the *Union Recorder.* Sidney Lanier was a relative and frequent visitor in the Nisbet home. Nina Nisbet moved to Tennessee after her marriage to William Poindexter Hambaugh.

Joseph Nisbet's sister, Emmie Nisbet, married Joseph LeConte, famous physician and geologist. He was professor at the University of Georgia, the College of South Carolina, and the University of California. Judge Eugenius A. Nisbet of the Supreme Court of Georgia, who wrote the Articles of Secession, was a great uncle of Miss Emmie's mother.

Miss Emmie has happy memories of visits in the home of her cousin, Harry Stillwell Edwards, and for many years she corresponded regularly with this distinguished writer.

Becuse of her generosity, Miss Emmie is flooded with mail for every conceivable cause. She donates to the Democarts and the Republicans. She could easily paper more than one wall with pictures of presidential candidates, presidents, and their families. She agrees with Rousseau that dead men carry in their cold fingers only that which they have given away.

Miss Emmie is in a position to admit she has "the gift of never realizing there is a generation gap between young people and me." So her own verse takes on more depth when she writes:

> For Youth is such a fleeting guest,
> And—must entertain
> Unwelcome though he be,
> Old age who makes of us
> Such caricatures of what
> We once have been.

At some time or other grief crosses the path of every living being. Miss Emmie's path has been no exception. After the death of her first husband, Howard Robinson, journalist on the *New York Sun,* she was left with a daughter and an unborn son. There were times of despair and doubt, but several years later, when her son Jim lay at the point of death, she prayed, "God, give me back my boy and I'll give my life to You." Her son's recovery was a miracle, and Miss Emmie has kept her promise.

On her ninetieth birthday Herbert Wilcox wrote that "Miss Emmie's outlook on life is pretty well expressed in a chant of the Navajo Indians, 'In an old age wandering on a trail of beauty, lively may I walk.' Clearly she finds her trail one of beauty, and she likes for her friends to share its joys with her."

In the stillness of her study or in the beauty of her garden, her words will not be forgotten: "I never borrow for tomorrow but I prepare for the future. . . . Always in life there will be a high crest and valley and you will find a crest again. You won't always be in the valley. Take the next crest of the wave and keep on. Don't give up."

1978

Author's note: Miss Emmie celebrated her one-hundredth birthday on June 29, 1986.

market, made this remark to me: "We had a nice profit, so decided to let the other fellow make a little."

To sum these up, "No business is better than the service that goes with it—provided that the service is of good quality—and be unselfish enough to let the other fellow make a little too."

—Clifford Smith

The Goose with Horse Sense & Other Animal Friends

Don't boast about
your pedigree.
Each squirrel has its
family tree.

—*Sarah Harbin*

Big John the goose loves to eat, and the Canadian geese, as well as all the other animals on the farm, keep their distance as Big John engages in his favorite pastime.

The Goose with Horse Sense

When some bird follows you, watch out. That is the opinion of Arnold Oglesby of Elberton, owner of Big John, a ten-year-old goose who follows his owner on land or lake. When Mr. Oglesby goes walking in the pasture in search of his cows, Big John trails him. If he goes fishing on one of his lakes, Big John either swims behind the boat or he flies overhead.

Big John will not allow anyone or any animal to come between him and Mr. Oglesby. If this error is made, fierce pecking is the penalty.

Every animal or bird on the Oglesby farm has learned to give Big John plenty of stretching room. The six Arabian horses, a pointer, a collie, the cows, the hogs, and an old gray cat have learned their place. When the gray cat comes and rubs against Big John, the goose promptly bites the cat's tail.

Although Big John cannot boast of any special pedigree, he is smart enough to be the lead bird for his companions, ten Canadian geese and three mallard ducks. Amazingly, they follow him on the lake in beautiful formation, just as if he were an admiral of the navy.

Big John can hear Mr. Oglesby's car approaching almost a mile away. He starts honking and flapping his wings, and he expects to be fed immediately upon his owner's arrival. He is especially fond of crackers, bread, and grain. Peanut butter makes him mad enough to peck hard. You cannot call him an unselfish bird, for he does not relish the idea of sharing his food.

When Big John takes his stand in the doorway of Mr. Oglesby's cabin on the lakes, nobody crosses that threshold. John Allgood of Elberton said that Big John was the best "watchdog" in Elbert County.

When Mr. Oglesby leaves the cabin, Big John follows his master about a half-mile to the highway. He flies over the car and then turns around and flies back to the lakes.

Cliff Arnold, uncle of Mr. Oglesby, reluctantly went back to Portland, Maine, to spend the summer. "I can't stand the heat here," he said, "but I can't stand to leave my best friend."

"Who, me?" questioned Mr. Oglesby.

"No, Big John. He is the smartest goose in the world. He might well have descended from the sacred geese that saved the city of Rome."

"I doubt that," said Arnold Oglesby. "Let's say Big John is just plain goose with a lot of horse sense."

1969

A Man and His Dog

(as recalled and told to Frank Wansley by his father, Leroy Hamilton Wansley)

During a revival meeting in a Ruckersville church, John L. Craft went down the aisle and got down on his knees at the altar. His old hound dog had followed him to church, and John didn't know that his dog had gone down the aisle too.

While John was praying, the dog started licking him in the face. John got up and kicked the dog out of the church. The pastor rebuked him severely. He said, "John, I never saw such cruelty to an animal. That dog is probably the best friend you've got."

The dog kicker replied, "But preacher, how in tarnation can a man pray with a dog lickin' him in his face?"

Rosebud

When a child needs waking up in the classroom, the solution may have four legs. If "meaningful criteria" and copious theories flap their wings and flop, just invite a pig to school. A pig named Rosebud.

You might say that Rosebud, a one-month-old Poland China pig, was a victim of compulsory education. She was happy enough with her four sisters, five brothers, and her mama in Union City, Georgia, but her owner, Vernon Suttles, gave his permission to photographer Rachel Whitmire for Rosebud to make a short visit to a Fulton County school in East Point, Georgia. The die was cast. What can a pig do but attend school when a permission slip is given?

When Rosebud the pig visited a school in East Point, Georgia, she became fast friends with those children who treated her gently, but she was quick to turn her aristocratic snout the other way when subjected to too much activity.

Rachel Whitmire

If Rosebud had been bussed clear across town in the usual way, she might have found the trip more pleasant. But confined to a metal carrier, she had reason to kick and grunt all the way to school. Naturally she was solemn and still when she was lifted out of the carrier and deposited in the fifth grade. The children, who moments before were not especially elated over new or ancient mathematics, jumped out of their seats in less time than it takes to say *pig*.

The Poland China Special kept her cool, and after weathering the first onslaught of the youngsters, strolled around to do special investigation. She sniffed desks and peered in to see what the children were reading. As she crawled under desks, the girls and boys did likewise. Rosebud had full command of the stage as if she were the prima donna at a great swine concert.

When the English language went unnoticed, the teacher resorted to Spanish and implored the students to get quiet and sit down. Result: no success. Fortunately Rosebud was multilingual, with a built-in understanding of Pig Latin, so Spanish proved no problem. The obedient little pig looked at the children in porky disapproval and immediately stopped grunting. She not only minded the teacher by sitting down, but she laid her black head on a boy's lap.

The piglet responded easily to the children who treated her gently, but she turned her aristocratic snout the other way when she was barraged by too much activity. Her tail became as straight as a row of peanuts in south Georgia when two boys made the error of pulling it. She was a Poland China *lady* and she abhorred ungentlemanly conduct. It took time and soft, tender words for the original curl to return.

Since the four-legged visitor showed such obvious obedience and intelligence, several fifth-graders were happy because they had previously chosen the pig to be the most intelligent and most easily trained animal. Other students had chosen cats, dogs, ponies, horses, monkeys, elephants, lions, and dolphins to be the most knowledgeable.

One girl was delighted when Rosebud drank only half a bottle of milk, for in her research she remembered that it is common sense to eat like a pig. Pigs never overeat. Neither do they overdrink.

After Rosebud left the schoolroom with the photographer and some unusually willing boys, the little shoat must have experienced the same uninhibited release that children feel on a playground. She raced around the field like a gazelle. Perhaps her ESP encouraged her to try out for the national physical fitness test. At the edge of the field was a steep embankment and she slid down in Olympic excellence with four boys in hot pursuit. At the bottom of the hill, the little black racer, red with dust, was retrieved by four equally dusty boys and was brought back to the photographer.

Rosebud *was* glad to return home to her family. Her sisters and brothers sniffed and gathered around her to see where she had been. Mama Pig showed true wisdom—love and no questions.

1978

Bob Chilles and His Bird Dog College

In a little white cottage just north of Elberton, Bob Chilles, a native of Scotland, proves that the word gets around if a dog trainer knows his business. Up till now not a line has ever been written about him or his dogs, and yet every year, sportsmen from many states find their way to his door.

When they reach his modest home, the chances are that the bachelor Scotsman will be in a state of unparalleled content. For oftentimes Bob is apt to be in bed reading dog lore while his own dogs lie around him dozing and dreaming about whatever fills a fine bird dog's dreams. That is, they will find this tranquil scene if it is late afternoon. Earlier in the day Bob and his dogs will be in the field.

Bob's first experience with bird dogs began in the "Auld Country" where as a young lad in Aberdeenshire, Scotland, he had a job as a game beater and drove birds out in the open for rich folk to shoot. Though dogs were used only to retrieve the wounded or dead birds on those Scotch preserves, they were fine dogs, and young Bob Chilles got the love of them in his blood. It has never left him.

Forty years ago Bob came to America and made his home in the North. His brother Bill kept painting such thrilling pictures about hunting down South that finally Bob yielded and in 1924 joined his brother in Elberton, where they began training and boarding dogs.

In reminiscing over his fine canine specimens, Bob recalls Rex, a pointer, who tipped the scales at eighty-five pounds. Though it took two years to train him, Rex was better than anything on four legs. His long graceful lope and motionless point would do any trainer proud. Then there was Buck, who has gone on to dog glory. If his master didn't come home at what he considered the correct time, Buck would paw the earth and howl, and if Bob was in reaching distance Buck would go after him and escort him home.

Last year one of Bob's dogs proved he had found a covey of birds, although the party of hunters had lost track of him. A long search for the dog found him still holding the point. "A hunter is lucky if this happens two or three times in a lifetime," the trainer remarked.

Nothing thrills the Scotsman more than young dogs. One usually knows what the old ones will do, but the young ones afford endless surprises.

Some dogs train naturally as soon as they are taken into the field. Others require two seasons, so Bob trains and boards these between seasons. He has found that if a dog is bred for hunting he doesn't need to be taught to hunt. "Just take him out in the field and teach him to obey and know what to expect. That is all. He'll do the rest," Bob promised.

"A dog reflects his trainer's personality," observed Bob. "A real trainer must control his own temper if he intends to control dogs, and if a dog has a mean disposition, the owner had better use a mirror."

The Elbertonian gives few rules for dog fanciers. "Study the dog's personality and find out why he does what he does. Never walk toward a dog in retrieving. Walk away. Never talk to a dog when he does as he should. Don't say, 'Steady, steady.' If he is already steady, why give him the jitters? In the field, don't talk to the dog or pet him."

Bob's dogs are managed almost entirely by sign language in the field. Dogs soon learn to watch for his signals rather than for loud commands.

As far as preference in pointers and setters go, Bob has none. "The pointer is better in hot weather and in an open field. The setter is better in cold weather, thorn fields and bushes, and the setter usually learns more easily than the pointer.

"From a money standpoint I'll never get rich in this dog business," mused Bob, "but from my heart's standpoint, I couldn't have any more riches. Yes, sir, man's most wonderful four-footed friend and companion is the dog."

1945

Taken for Granite

Well, that's just
another way that
Elberton has of
advertising granite.

*—Corra Harris, upon seeing
the granite marker erected in
her honor at Farm Hill, her
girlhood home*

*The Georgia Guidestones
monument in Elbert County carries
ten engraved messages in English,
Spanish, Mandarin Chinese,
Arabic, Classical Hebrew, Swahili,
Hindi, and Russian.*

A Guidestones Monument
for Elberton

The tales of buried gold in Elbert County will never lose their luster, but now a newer mystery envelops Elberton, the Little International City that is the Granite Capital of the World. On one of the highest hills in Elbert County, off Highway 77, a granite monument has been erected to serve as a guide for mankind.

The Georgia Guidestones monument carries ten engraved messages in English, Spanish, Mandarin Chinese, Arabic, Classical Hebrew, Swahili, Hindi, and Russian. It is over nineteen feet high and is composed of six massive pieces of granite weighing more than eighty-eight tons. Over the four upright slabs of granite, a capstone is inscribed in Sanskrit, Babylonian cuneiform, classical Greek, and Egyptian hieroglyphics: "Let These Be Guidestones to an Age of Reason."

With oblique holes drilled at precise angles in the central stone, the monument's astronomical features permit the noontime sun to record the time of day and year. The ten guides are:

MAINTAIN HUMANITY UNDER 500,000,000
  IN PERPETUAL BALANCE WITH NATURE

GUIDE REPRODUCTION WISELY—
  IMPROVING FITNESS AND DIVERSITY

UNITE HUMANITY WITH A LIVING LANGUAGE

RULE PASSION—FAITH—TRADITION—
  AND ALL THINGS
    WITH TEMPERED REASON

PROTECT PEOPLE AND NATIONS
  WITH FAIR LAWS AND JUST COURTS

LET ALL NATIONS RULE INTERNALLY
RESOLVING EXTERNAL DISPUTES
IN A WORLD COURT
AVOID PETTY LAWS AND USELESS OFFICIALS
BALANCE PERSONAL RIGHTS WITH SOCIAL DUTIES
PRIZE TRUTH—BEAUTY—LOVE—
SEEKING HARMONY WITH THE INFINITE
BE NOT A CANCER ON THE EARTH—
LEAVE ROOM FOR NATURE—
LEAVE ROOM FOR NATURE

Only Wyatt Martin, president of the Granite City Bank, knows the identity of those who paid for the monument through an escrow account.

So, like the mystery of the buried gold in Elbert County, "Let others probe the mystery if they can."

1980

In Granite

Why should young people leave Elberton for faraway places—especially if their families are, as old-timers say, *in granite?* Many who leave to seek their fortune elsewhere are smart enough to come back home to green pastures on a solid foundation—Elberton's $40 million-a-year granite business.

From the outset this industry has been recognized as a family affair. There are husband-wife teams plus their offspring, father-son companies, father-daughter affiliations, with a generous sprinkling of cousins and enterprising in-laws.

William A. Kelly, executive vice-president of the Elberton Granite Association and editor of the *Elberton Graniteer*, says there are many incentives for the career-minded to look toward the Granite Capital of the World. Last year the Elberton Granite Center building was greatly expanded to serve members in Elberton and their customers throughout the United States and foreign countries.

Adjacent to the Granite Center, a new multi-purpose Elberton Granite Museum has been built. It provides exhibit space on three separate levels, and a specially equipped classroom, library, and archives room. The first gift to the Granite Museum was a vast collection of pictures taken by the late Everett Saggus, master of photography. Before his death he gave the museum thousands of pictures depicting the history of the granite industry.

In 1980 those in granite applauded the construction of a water jet machine, which is a dramatic new method of removing stone from the earth. And now in full operation is a recently constructed Granite Laboratory at the Elbert County Comprehensive High School, which offers classes in basic principles of monument manufacturing.

Undoubtedly folks *in granite* have reason to believe in a firm foundation.

1980

Grave Humor

George T. Oglesby of Elberton attributes much of his success to early parental advice and hard work. He well remembers his father's words, "Son, take one step at a time but be sure where you put your feet." And the son not only did just that but in choosing a career he put his foot on a firm foundation, *granite*.

He began working for the Elberton Granite Industry in the 1930s. He later bought half-interest in a finishing plant and in two years became its owner. In 1959 he went into the quarrying business. His son Tom joined him in business in 1967. Father and son make a good working team. George T., as president of Keystone Granite Company, looks after quarrying activities, and son Tom, president of Keystone Memorials, Inc., concentrates on management of monument manufacturing.

In 1983 they moved to a mammoth new ultramodern production complex on the Washington Highway two miles south of Elberton. Visitors from many states and foreign countries have toured this facility, which is one of the nation's leading monument finishing firms. In 1982 Keystone Memorials purchased the Missouri Red Granite Quarry in Missouri. A new building at the Galleria in Atlanta has recently been built of Missouri Red granite.

Being "in granite" can well be considered a serious profession as well as a grave one, but fortunately it does have a lighter side.

Several years ago George T. Oglesby made national headlines when he set up a 73-piece, 100-ton exhibit at a posh hotel at Miami Beach. It was "sort of a trade show" for the annual gathering of the American Monument Association and the Monument Builders of North America. Vacationers who were on their way to the swimming pool were not too happy about trudging through the gravestones and seeing flying angels all about.

The desk clerk reported that an elderly man called downstairs and said he woke up in a festive mood after getting a good night's sleep. But when he looked out the window and saw an instant cemetery he plopped back into bed, thoroughly flabbergasted.

"Fortunately most of the complaints were lighthearted," Oglesby said. "We even had people trying to buy or order some of the monuments."

Every day presents its own surprise. One morning George T. was called to his office to see a customer who wanted to buy a pre-need monument. "The man told me that he had investigated my company and me, and we met his specifications. He said he had no relatives and had only a maximum of six months to live. He assured me he was not only financially able to live comfortably his allotted time but he was also able to make the proper provisions for his death. I accepted the order and gave the customer a copy of the contract to be sent to his funeral director in Orlando, Florida. When he paid cash for the order, I tried to get a forwarding address. He objected, saying that he trusted me, and that where he was going he would have no need of a forwarding address."

A number of years ago an elderly lady purchased a companion monument after her husband's death. When the contract was being written she said, "Just go on and put my death date too. Make it the same year my husband died." The Oglesbys don't know whether or not she timed her departure correctly.

Today there is a large increase in markers of historical significance and monuments to commemorate war veterans. Many outstanding works of art in granite show the sculptor's skill.

The inscriptions on monuments often reflect a serious tone. They may include a Bible quotation from Job: "I know that my redeemer liveth," or some lines from Shakespeare: "To me, fair friend, you never can be old, / For as you were when first your eye I ey'd, / Such seems your beauty still." And from an old Persian Proverb: "What I kept I lost, / What I spent I had, / What I gave I have."

According to son Tom, not all inscriptions assume angelic proportions. "Recently we did a tree stump for a customer in Michigan. In Louisiana one monument had pigs, chickens, mules, and a man holding a chain saw with a tree falling over.

"Last year a woman from Kentucky wanted a monument erected. On one side she wanted to duplicate the last birthday card that she sent her husband Chester before his demise. And on the other side of the monument she wanted to duplicate the last birthday card that Chester sent to her."

The Oglesbys won't easily forget checking this unusual monument. High on a hill on a dirt road in Kentucky they found that the birthday memorial met proper specifications.

Epitaphs are as unexpected as they are revealing. One marker shipped to Tennessee had this message: "Ain't no grave gonna hold this body down." A marker installed in Iowa had this inscription: "I'VE LED A WILD LIFE BOYS / BUT I'VE EARNED ALL I SPENT / I PAID ALL I BORROWED / AND I LOST ALL I LENT / I ONCE LOVED A WOMAN / AND THAT CAME TO AN END / SO GET A GOOD DOG BOYS / IT WILL BE YOUR BEST FRIEND."

One man admitted that his wife had always had the last word in any argument. When she departed this earth he was finally able to voice an opinion. This is the inscription in memory of his wife: "MY WIFE'S GONE / BUT I'M NOT BLUE / SHE'S RESTING NOW / AND I AM TOO.

George T. recalls a seven-word epitaph that he will not forget: "SAVED BY GRACE IF SAVED AT ALL."

1985

Dutchy, Elberton's First Granite Statue

Elberton's first granite finishing plant was built in 1898 for "the sole purpose of completing a Confederate monument for the Public Square in Elberton."

According to a story in *Georgia Scribe*, written by the late Herbert Wilcox, the memorial was sponsored by the ladies of the Confederate Memorial Association.

The *Elberton Star* of July 22, 1898, gave the following account of the unveiling of the Confederate monument:

"Last Friday morning, July 15, ere the sun had risen far above the horizon the streets of our little city presented a busy appearance. Carriages, buggies, wagons, carts of all descriptions, horseback riders and muleback riders, and throngs of pedestrians were pouring in from every quarter. . . .

"The beautiful and attractive Miss Roberta Heard arose and gracefully walked to the front of the platform accompanied by her maids of honor, all beautiful young girls tastefully attired in white organdies, and while the band played a soft martial air the veil fell from the granite soldier and he stood proudly facing the immense crowd.

"After the unveiling the band struck up a march and pretty little flower girls in their dainty white dresses and baskets of flowers, led by the graceful little sylph, Miss Em Mai Tate, marched around the monument and strewed their floral offerings.

"The young ladies who assisted Miss Roberta Heard were: Misses Annie McCalla, Dot Shannon, Hammond Burch, Edna Arnold, Jessie Roberts, Mary Jim Cason, and Louise McIntosh. The flower girls were: Em Mai Tate, Bernice Blackwell, Ethel Willis, Jennie Ray Auld, Florence Brown, Maud Brown, Irene Stilwell, Mattie Carrie Heard, Camilla Pharr, Marguerite Brewer, Zelma Allen and Mary Alexander."

The main body of the monument was a real work of art, but beyond a doubt the soldier placed on top of the monument did not meet the sanction or approval of Elbertonians. Soon after the unveiling the soldier was nicknamed *Dutchy*, and Dutchy will always have the distinction of being Elberton's *first* granite statue.

The sculptor, Arthur Beter, was believed to have been an immigrant, and he was obviously unacquainted with the differences in Civil War uniforms. Dutchy wore a cap and a tunic blouse that was a far cry from any resemblance to the Confederate uniform, but bore a remarkable similarity to the uniform of a Union soldier. Herbert Wilcox wrote: "There were hundreds of veterans still living and they declared that the Confederate army never had anything that looked like him or the uniform he wore."

What goes up can, with a rope, come down, so two years after the unveiling, seven-foot-tall Dutchy tumbled to the ground with the help of displeased citizens who placed a rope around him and toppled him to the ground.

The *Star* of August 16, 1900, gave this account: "Dutchy is no more. The man with the stoney glare in his eyes took a tumble Monday night and is now lying in the middle of the square with two broken limbs . . ." Poor Dutchy. He was reduced to disgrace and was buried facedown at the foot of the monument.

But—can one who falls rise again? Yes—with the help of his fellow man. And on April 28, 1982, with the help of the Elberton Granite Association and many fellow men, Dutchy was dug up from his resting place on the Public Square. Old-timers came to the rescue of E.G.A.'s Bill Kelly and told him where to dig, and under his direction, the digging began on a rainy day.

After about two hours Dutchy was unearthed. And what a day it was! People came from far and near to witness the Great Dig. Many observers wanted to know how a statue would look after being buried in Georgia's red clay for eighty-two years. A quick bath in a local car wash plus more cleaning with high pressure water revealed Dutchy, a granite statue like new. Folks

Hudson Cone

Dutchy, Elberton's first granite statue, was first erected in 1898. He was resurrected in 1982 and now lies in the Elberton Granite Museum.

agreed that Dutchy's appearance provided the best advertisement for *Elberton Granite*.

So Dutchy went on to his new home at the E.G.A.'s Granite Museum and is deservedly the central attraction.

If Dutchy could talk he no doubt would express pride in being the first cog in the wheel of Elberton's multimillion-dollar granite industry. Sharing equal honors with Dutchy is the late Peter Bertoni, who came into the possession of the plant in which Dutchy was created. Bertoni is considered to be the father of the granite-finishing business in Elberton.

The story of Dutchy's rise, fall, and resurrection may serve as an instrument of peace, and Dutchy may be just the one needed to heal old wounds, no matter what garb he wears.

Author's note: The spacious Elberton Granite Museum & Exhibit opened in 1981 and contains historical exhibits, artifacts, educational displays, and materials depicting current and past events in the rich heritage of the Elberton granite industry. The museum also features the latest in audiovisual equipment for entertaining and informative film presentations and slide shows.

The museum is located adjacent to the Elberton Granite Association's Granite Center headquarters building on College Avenue, one-half mile west of downtown Elberton. There is no admission charge. For further information call 404-283-2551.

"The Man on the Ledge"

by William A. Kelly,
Executive Vice-President of Elberton Granite Association

Elberton's Granite Industry provides employment for 1,700 persons who are all dependent on "The Man on the Ledge."

Elberton's thirty granite quarries and fifty-six granite manufacturing plants turn out twenty-two million dollars of granite products each year. This production would be zero were it not for "The Man on the Ledge."

Over 150,000 monuments, markers, and mausoleums are made of Elberton Granite annually . . . but each and every unit has its beginning with "The Man on the Ledge."

Who, then, is this "Man on the Ledge" on whom so much depends? He is, indeed, the "forgotten man" of the industry . . . but in truth, he may well deserve to be known as the "most important man" in the industry.

Go to any quarry and view the awesomeness of the giant caverns in the earth . . . look up at the towering steel derricks . . . marvel at the steep walls of stone. This is the habitat of "The Man on the Ledge" with his sinewy muscles, his powerful brawn, his body glistening with sweat, his sheer strength apparent in his every move. This is the basic force that starts all Elberton Granite monuments on their long journey from the quarry to the cemetery. This initial energy is always provided by "The Man on the Ledge."

Machines perform many tasks in Elberton's Granite Industry . . . tasks that formerly were accomplished by hand. But no machine can ever take the place of the hands of the man who must guide the drill . . . who must position the holes in just the right place . . . who must know the proper time to apply the right physical force. No machine can replace the mighty grip on the weighty sledgehammer as it drives the shims and wedges in place. No machine can replace the knowing eye and the unerring response of the muscles of the man who first comes in contact with the raw stone. No machine can replace this "Man on the Ledge."

Look for this man on the streets of Elberton after his day's work is done. He may well be shirtless, showing his manly physique to the world . . . or he may have the tough but casual manner of the cowboy of long ago . . . or he may exhibit the concerned . . . or unconcerned . . . manner of a modern young American. In any case, this man will be readily recognizable from his enviable appearance . . . powerful chest . . . muscular arms . . . straight bearing . . . healthful smile. Attributes of a person who takes pride in his body and his manly prowess, these are truly the physical characteristics of "The Man on the Ledge."

All persons who derive their livelihood from granite—be he stonecutter, polisher, sandblaster, supervisor, owner, trucker, bookkeeper, retailer—should give the belated recognition due to the dedicated employee who toils in the quarries in the hot summer sun, through the cold days of winter, in fair weather and foul. His is the basic task in the Granite Industry. Without him, there would be no stone to cut or polish, no crates to transport, no business to own or operate, and no beautiful memorials to admire as the final product of so many labors.

A salute, then, is in order to the man who is the essential beginning cog in the production wheel of Elberton's Granite Industry. May his strength endure . . . may his fortitude last . . . may his vital role be better understood by all concerned . . . and may his rightful recognition be accorded to the person who truly fills a most important role in every respect for everyone connected with the memorial business. A hearty and long overdue salute to—"The Man on the Ledge."

Poke Salad, Sassafras Tea, & Scuppernong Vines

"Take your cuttings on the new of the moon. Don't laugh at this advice. Even the ocean obeys the moon."

—*Ella Carter*

Poke Salad and Sassafras Tea, or Nature's Remedies

And suddenly it's spring. A time to choose a revitalizing booster. Which will it be—a cup of sassafras tea or a newfangled pill or capsule? This may well be the right year to lend an ear to the wonders of old-fashioned tonics and remedies.

In Georgia, sassafras tea was synonymous with springtime. Herbert Wilcox of Elberton recalls that for one week in the early spring his family drank sassafras tea for breakfast. Others believed in drinking it daily for the first month of spring. Some preferred cherry-bark tea and fever tea for toning up the body.

To purify the blood, a combination of sulfur and molasses was hard to beat. One ninety-three-year-old Elbertonian is living proof that nature's remedies work. She praises the medicinal properties of dried pipsissewa, a bitter herb found in the woods. Pine tonic is another spring booster. The recipe is simple enough. In the fall or winter, put lightwood into a big bucket of water, and next spring drink the tonic water.

In days gone by and even today, children and grownups find poke salad, turnip greens, onions, and garlic far more pleasant as cleansing agents than some other doses. The poke salad's tender leaves are boiled, and usually the first water is poured off, since it is thought to be poisonous. Drinking garlic juice cleanses the blood, loosens stiff joints, and lowers blood pressure.

Spring is a time to look for mullein leaves, an old-time cure for leg swelling and sprained ankles. These big, collard-like leaves can be boiled and wrapped around the leg, ankle, or foot.

Georgians have always believed in going fishing in the spring and, in days gone by, would eat nothing but fish for seven consecutive days. There is an old tradition that if a man and woman fish together and catch two fish simultaneously, it may lead to matrimony.

By the way, some Georgians advise taking a spring tonic and selecting a mate when the moon is full.

1976

"I'll Meet You Under the Scuppernong Vine"

"I'll meet you under the scuppernong vine" is about the most welcome promise a Georgian can offer to a friend, and it is a promise that seldom goes unfulfilled. The only question that arises is a wishful "How soon?" No possum hunt or watermelon cutting affords half the opportunity as does the socially significant scuppernong in bringing together country folks, city cousins, and ever-so-slight acquaintances.

The man named Webster reveals that the scuppernong received its name from the Scuppernong River in North Carolina, it is an American grape, large, yellow-green in color, and a form of vitis rotundifolia. But Georgians could tell old man Noah something when they start poking through the vines and bring down a double handful of yellow-brown jewels that disappear as quickly as they meet the mouth.

Georgia boasts of vines fruitful after a century of bearing, and in late summer, grapeless unfortunates turn their heads toward the country and visit the same vines that they have frequented for years. Many of these famous vines are thirty to one hundred years old.

Years ago during scuppernong season numerous signs could be found around the state which read: "Eat all you can for 10 cents." From an observing and partaking point of view, the "all you can eat" is practically limitless for the majority of consumers. Men, women, and children would line up and plink their dimes into an old tin bucket and pop scuppernongs and scatter hulls to their heart's content. From a flavor standpoint, early morning, before the sun hits the vine, is the best time for eating them, but from a get-together angle, the cool of the evening provides the best time for social relish.

A distaste for scuppernongs is unheard of, and no one has been known to get sick from eating too many, whether he practices the efficient Georgia technique of leaving the seeds within the hulls or whether he prefers the plumb-all method of eating the pulp, seeds, and even the hulls.

Around the vines there are usually children who have reached the brim of plenty and who feel the urge to shower scuppernong hulls at the eaters. More than likely, however, the slip-showing, shirt-tailed, short-clad, slack-wearing pickers are too busily engaged in their own pursuits to be upset over a mere hailstorm of hulls.

Government bulletins advise training the vines on a trellis. Georgians did not take this advice hastily, but today, with a large increase of vines on trellises, there is evidence that the scuppernong arbor is a page out of the past.

Scuppernongs, like humans, come in trousered and petticoated varieties, but the latter, true to the age-old custom, is the one that pays off by producing the fruit. The male vine, however, adhering to the usual rule, is essential to the grape-producing program. Throughout Georgia there is usually a manly vine in the woods according to nature's needs, but where scuppernongs are grown commercially, a male vine is planted to every four or five females. New vines, of either sex, are produced by rooting runners of established vines. Vines have to be handled with diplomacy, for they resent being moved or pruned at the wrong season, and they promptly respond by bleeding to death. They are ageless, however, if they are treated humanly. If muscadines are desired, the amateur can try his luck by planting seeds from scuppernongs.

Scuppernong wine, spun-gold in color and effect, is one of Georgia's most popular wines. In former years good sound church members made scuppernong wine yearly to be used for communion services. The story is told that one deacon eased back in the church after the communion service and finished the remaining wine. As a result he showed more religious fervor than his less indulging friends.

Summer cannot slip by without Georgia housewives putting up jar upon jar of scuppernong and muscadine jelly and preserves, and a favorite old-fashioned dessert is a hot buttered biscuit with an ample helping of tangy muscadine preserves.

Whether arbor or trellis, the delightful smell of the scuppernong beckons to the lover of its fruit. And when the sun sends its slanting rays autumnward, Georgia is the place to be.

1968

The Gift, a Short Story

Mary Laney squiggled her toes in the soil where Mr. Whipple had carefully planted his Irish potatoes. She could not understand the soft mysterious words he murmured into the earth.

His eyes travelled from the potato row to the onion row. His smile was big enough to include a little girl in his garden.

"So you know why they need each other?" he asked.

"Who, Mr. Whipple?"

"My potatoes and onions. You see, when summer comes, it usually gets so carried away with sunshine and fun, that it forgets that plants are thirsty. Like you, when you run and jump and play too long. When the potatoes' throats get dry, the onions shed tears of sympathy for their neighbor."

"How long do the onions cry?" she asked.

"Until the potatoes drink their fill," he said.

Mary Laney looked Mr. Whipple straight in the eye. "Is that really so?" she questioned.

The old man picked up some soil and let it sift through his hands.

"Yes, honey, that's the way it is."

"Will you promise me something?" she begged.

"If I can."

"The next time I feel sad, will you plant me some onions?"

"Little girls like you are meant for joy," he answered with a smile.

As the clouds swirled their fleecy folds across the late afternoon sky, Mary knew it was time to go. Her mother would be calling. Mary leaned down to the earth and placed her left ear against a freshly plowed furrow.

"Do you hear anything?" he asked.

She wrinkled her nose. "No, I don't, Mr. Whipple. Not a sound."

"Come back, child. You will hear. Hearing comes from growing. Some day you will hear the song of the earth."

Mary walked slowly home. What did he mean? Did the earth sing? Did seeds sing? And if they did what did they say?

She sat down on the back door steps, removed her shoes and cleaned the dirt off. Mr. Whipple's dirt. But Mr. Whipple said it did not really belong to him. It was borrowed—from someone greater than he.

Mrs. Laney was setting the table. She turned and said, "My little helper forgot to help her mother today."

"I'm sorry, Mother, but I'll make up for it. I promise I will."

At the table Mr. Laney asked the blessing, and when he included a prayer for all the world, Mary's little shoulders rested comfortably against her chair.

The next afternoon Mary went to Adams Seed Store. As she entered, Mr. Rafferty came forward. Mary was his favorite visitor. "What's on your mind today, Mary?"

She blew a wisp of hair that kept riding over her left eyebrow. "I'm looking for seeds that talk," she said.

Mr. Rafferty chuckled. Do you want a big sound or a little sound? "Now, take a butter bean. It's bold and brave. You can hear it the length of Jack's beanstalk."

"Did Mr. Whipple tell you his secret?"

"Well, no, he didn't. You have to do your own listening. You must be very still and very patient."

"If I plant morning glory seeds, will I be able to hear the morning glories grow?"

Mr. Rafferty puckered his brow. "You can try."

"Mr. Whipple has morning glories that stay open all day for him. Why is that?"

"Mr. Whipple is a very special man and he knows how to talk to all things that grow. He is the earth's friend, and when he insists on the morning glories blooming a little longer, they feel honored to do so."

"My mother's birthday is the twenty-second of May, and I want to give her the prettiest flower of all."

"Give her the rose, my dear."

He took her by the hand and wandered down a path of roses. There were red ones red as the heart of a valentine. There were pink ones as pink as the toes of a little baby kicking for joy in his crib. There were yellow roses that traced golden swaths toward the shining sun. There were the white roses that bloomed with all the beauty of purity.

She touched the petals of a red rose. "I want this for my mother," she said. She handed him her worldly possessions, a dime, a nickel, and ten pennies.

Mr. Rafferty shook his head. "No, Mary. Roses grow better when they are given. Keep that money and some day it will help to build a steeple."

Mary reached up and hugged Mr. Rafferty. "Thank you, oh, thank you!" As she raced home she held the rose bush very close to her ear. Just in case—

She was glad Mr. Whipple was in his garden. She liked to hear him grumble, especially when he was talking to crabgrass. Now that was something he did not like at all. "Every living thing should know its place and crabgrass never has learned that lesson," he said sternly. When he saw the rose bush his eyes lost their disgruntled look. "What have you got there, honey?"

"It's for my mother's birthday. Do you think it will bloom in May?"

"It will if it's for your mother. I have prepared a row in my garden just for you. I've even named it for you. Come, let's give your rose bush a comfortable place to stretch and grow and sing a song of living."

Across the way Mr. Claiborne's goats nibbled on whatever they could find. They stuck their inquisitive noses through the fence as the last bit of dirt was cushioned around the rose bush.

Weeks flew by. Mr. Whipple said that plants grow best when you give them something you prize, so Mary took her favorite doll Miranda and propped her rag doll friend against the bush. Miranda would make anything grow. She was the kind of doll who understood. Mr. Whipple often wrote poems and tucked them under the folds of earth, so Mary wrote these lines:

If the walnut shell is extra heavy and the corn shucks are heavy, bundle up. You can look out for a hard cold winter.

—Old-time Georgia superstition

"To my mother, who can probably hear seeds pop, because she can hear all things and do all things." She folded the paper and put it in the soil far enough down so it could take firm root—if it would. Then she dug a hole beside the rose bush and carefully planted her worldly possessions. Mr. Rafferty might be right. Perhaps a steeple might grow.

On May the twenty-first Mary Laney's heart was filled with joy, for there was a rose in bloom for her mother's gift. The next morning Mary got up long before anyone thought of rising. As the morning sun tipped the garden with promise, she stood staring at the rose bush. The crimson gift was gone. Only a small stalk stood as a reminder of where the rose had been. Miranda was sitting helplessly beside the stalk. Her little calico dress was chewed to shreds.

Mr. Claiborne's goats peered at her reflectively. No one had told them of the importance of giving gifts to someone you love. As Mary reached down to pick up Miranda something nudged her on the arm. With a start she looked up and found a goat standing close beside her. He nibbled at her sleeve. Tears streaked down Mary's face and fell on Miranda's shoulder. Miranda had long since learned how to adjust to laughter or tears.

At school Miss Brown reprimanded Mary for not being able to tell a noun from a verb. Why couldn't Miss Brown understand that sometimes parts of speech don't really matter! The unhappy child put her head down on her desk. Mercifully Miss Brown let her rest.

After the last bell had rung, Mr. Whipple waited at the gate for his little neighbor. Mary's wan face had only a shadow of a smile. His arms reached out to receive the sobbing child. "Oh, Mr. Whipple," she cried. "Oh, Mr. Whipple."

"Come, Mary, let's walk down the pasture lane. There's no place in the world like a pasture lane." Jonathan the robin accompanied them. He always kept a respectful distance behind them. There were things he needed to investigate along the way.

Far down the lane Mr. Whipple stopped. There beneath his feet bloomed a little flower. "The first bluet," he whispered. "The first bluet! How hushed the sound! Soft it pushes from the ground and blossoms all alone."

The little bluet stretched upward to hear the voice of one who knew the secret song of the earth. Mr. Whipple kneeled down. He placed his ear against the earth.

Somewhere in the far off corners of the earth there began a soft stirring. Like the bursting of a petal. Perhaps it was the wind in the trees. Or butterflies trying their wings for the first time.

Was it the bluet, the first bluet? Mary leaned far down to catch the smallest sound. "Do not pick me," the bluet seemed to say. "Let me live and grow in the pasture lane. Some day you will hear my song."

Jonathan the robin dutifully followed his two friends as they turned their steps toward home. When they came to Mr. Whipple's garden, Jonathan made a happy chirping sound as he spread his wings in flight. He circled the garden and came to rest on one of the limbs of Mary's rose bush. There in the May sunshine bloomed a rose as red as a rose can be.

Mary uttered a cry of delight. "But how, Mr. Whipple? How *did* it bloom again?"

Mr. Claiborne's goats came as close as the fence would allow. They cocked their ears to one side.

Mr. Whipple turned his face skyward as Jonathan spread his wings. The robin flew higher and higher into the sky. "There are ways, my child. Wondrous ways."

Mary Laney smiled and squiggled her toes in the luxuriant earth. Deep within her heart was the sound of music to match the beauty of her gift.

Planting by the Signs

There is really no need to run out and buy expensive equipment for home gardening. All one needs is a shovel, a rake, and a hoe, and if a gardener follows directions given by the seed companies, he may have a plentiful supply for his family and his neighbors.

But if a lover of the soil lends an ear to folklore, superstitions, and suggestions of old-timers, he may have a garden worth bragging about!

Some old-timers believe that if corn is planted when the moon is full, there will be stalks strong enough to support big, upstanding ears. If, however, corn is planted on a new moon, a stepladder will be needed to climb the stalks, but the ears won't be worth the climb. Almost every signologist will advise against planting on the first day of the new moon or on a day when the moon changes quarters.

Irish potatoes should be planted during the dark of the moon, and since they are known to be as sensitive and as retaliatory as human beings, the gardener is advised against skimping on the size of the piece of potato he plants. Some farmers, seasoned with years of experimentation and know-how, plant small whole potatoes for a supply guaranteed to impress.

Moonologists believe that the onion prefers to be planted under the dark of the moon, as do radishes, carrots, and turnips. Never forget the onion, for in its afterscent, it has long been considered a remedy against all pestilence, plague, and illness.

Those who have sound faith in old ideas and a genuine love for tomatoes in all seasons may enjoy them from early spring until the bite of winter, provided they plant tomato seeds after seeing a blood-red sunset on three successive days. If the moon is woolled over by a cloud or fog for five days in a row, then it is wise to wait and plant when the fog disappears. For the gardener who wants to be first in producing tomato plants, fruit jars can be used to cover the young plants. But it must be remembered that the jars should be removed when cold weather in the morning has unclenched its grip.

If the gardener has had poor luck in his planting, he is advised against planting on Friday. If, however, he is determined to plant on this day, he must complete whatever job he undertakes and put his gardening tools where they belong. The more reverent and more dedicated gardeners steadfastly believe in success with nature when they plant their gardens on Good Friday, come rain, sleet, or snow. And subsequently, they usually have proof to substantiate their schedule.

Saturday planting is supposed to bring a wagonload or at least a wheelbarrow full of vegetables and luck, but only on one condition—that no neighbors or friends come to visit on this particular day.

Some gardeners severely advise against planting or grafting on Sunday. On the other hand, some believe that the seventh day in the week provides special blessings upon seeds, plants, soil, and the gardener.

Some old-timers say that the weather will be good for planting if, in March, four squirrels run up a tree between six and ten in the morning or if more than one crow caws before seven o'clock. If rain is needed, look high and low for lambs lying down in a meadow.

Feverish gardeners believe that hot red pepper should be planted when a fellow is angry. Cynics have a right to smile sideways when superstitious farmers plant sweet pepper when they are in a loving mood.

Watermelon seeds should be soaked in sugar water (regardless of spiraling prices) before they are planted. Old-time farmers advise against planting them where sugar cane was grown. There's no doubt about it. The watermelon won't taste like a Georgia watermelon should.

Cane seeds and peanuts yield more abundantly when planted on the full moon in April. Researchers have found that the lordly English peas resent being planted too far away to communicate and often refuse to appear above the ground if they cannot be cozily situated.

Folks who have weathered many a year are prone to offer free advice. When a fellow gets a stomachache after eating cucumbers and radishes, don't call a doctor. Just be sure to return all borrowed garden tools to friends and neighbors. Result: no lengthy gastronomic disturbances and no doctor's bill.

Cabbage plants have sufficient courage to stand up for what they believe in, but gardeners long attuned to the ways of the soil still whisper into the collards' ears the magic words that scare away the calico bug.

1975

Love and Marriage

"Of all the home remedies, a good wife is the best of all."

—*Frank Wansley*

No Learned Wives Wanted

Male Students at the University of Georgia Agree on This Qualification of the Ideal Mate as Described in "The South Carolina and Georgia Almanack" of 1781. But Modern Co-Eds Favor Husbands of Superior Intellect, Who Shave Regularly

What are the qualifications of an ideal wife?

What goes to make a model husband?

How do young people today answer these questions?

How do their answers compare with those of a century or more ago?

In 1935 there was found on the campus of the University of Georgia a yellowed copy of "The South Carolina and Georgia Almanack," published in 1781, in which there are separate chapters on "the mental and personal qualifications" of husband and wife. The year of this rare book's publication, 1781, it will be remembered, is four years prior to the date of the chartering of the university—1785. It is interesting to compare the "qualifications" as set forth in this almanac with the views of student leaders on the Georgia campus 150 years later.

A good husband, according to the 1781 publication, should have

great good Nature, good Humour, and good Sense—Lively by all Means, Stupid by no Means. His Person agreeable rather than handsome. No great Objection to 6 Feet with an exact Symmetry of Parts. Always clean, but not foppish in his Dress. Youth promises a Duration of Happiness, therefore is agreeable. Well read in the Classics, but no Pedant. A tolerable Ear for Music, but no Fiddler. No Bully; just as much Courage as is necessary to defend his own and his Wife's Honour. No traveller; no Enthusiasm for the Vertu. ....May Fortune smile on the Man of my Wishes..........A Freethinker in every Thing, except in Matters of Religion..........These, with Mr. Pope's Definition of Wit, are the only qualifications I require in the Man I intend to honour with my Hand and Heart.

A wife, says this guide, should have

great good Nature, and a prudent Generosity. A lively Look, a proper Spirit, and a cheerful Disposition. A good Person, but not perfectly beautiful. Of a moderate Height. With regard to complexion, not quite fair, but a little brown..........Young by all Means..........Old by no Means. A decent Share of common Sense, just tinctured with a little seasonable Repartee, and a small Modicum of Wit, but no Learning, no Learning, I say again and again (either ancient or modern), upon any Consideration whatever. Well, but not critically skilled in her own Tongue.

In Spelling, a little becoming Deficiency, and in the Doctrine of Punctuation (or what is generally called Stopping), by no means conversant. A proper Knowledge of Accounts and Arithmetic, but no Sort of Skill in Fractions. No Enthusiasm for the Guitar. Ready at her Needle, but more devoted to plain Work than to fine. No Enemy to Knitting. Not always in the Parlour, but sometimes in the Kitchen. An Acquaintance with Domestic News, but no Acquaintance with foreign. Decently, but not affectedly, silent.

The phraseology of these statements differs, widely, of course, from that of the modern student, but do the ideas?

Helen Geffen of Atlanta, president of Women's Student Government Association, says that she wants a well-built man of average height. "As far as personal appearance is concerned, I require neatness above all. I want intelligence and intellect combined with a sociable personality, and I want him to have a definite religious faith. I like clever people. People who are on their toes all the time."

Callender Weltner, daughter of Chancellor Philip R. Weltner, has "no great objection to six feet" and a good physique. "I want a well-read man, one who enjoys being with a crowd, likes to play bridge, and likes to travel. He must have money or good prospects of having some. Above all, I'd like for him to have good taste in everything."

An interesting opinion was voiced by Mabel Stephens, daughter of Dr. R. P. Stephens, professor of mathematics and dean of the graduate school. "He doesn't have to be handsome, but he must keep shaved," she declares. "I like a comfortably dressed man, not one who has just stepped out of a band-box. I had rather he would have general information than a vast amount of education. I want a person who knows when to be reserved and when to be lively, depending on the occasion."

Ida Mogul, associate editor of the *Red and Black*, says, "I am interested in a man whose intelligence is far above the average, whose interests are the same as mine, and who isn't so good-looking that I will have to worry about him. I shall be satisfied with half of what I ask for, so long as he recognizes my merits."

Ruth Roberts, of Atlanta, discloses the fact that men of a dark type who are "practically" six feet tall interest her. "I want a good all-round man, but not necessarily an athletic one. He must be smart, but not brilliant, and he must have a good sense of humor. I want one who is thoughtful, and by all means faithful, but deliver me from a temperamental man."

"I want a rather indifferent man, but a very thoughtful one," says Marjorie Gould of Atlanta. "He must have high ideals. He must be a good business manager, but not have a mania for the subject. He can drink, if in moderation and not around me, but, most of all, he must be crazy about me."

"I'd rather he'd be nice-looking," says Alice Morrow, daughter of Dr. P. R. Morrow, associate professor of education at Georgia. "He must be a good sport, and very intelligent. I would like for him to be content to stay at home and go to a movie occasionally—provided—that I accompany him."

The men students on the campus were quite voluble on the subject of model mates. DeNean Stafford, president of Pan-Hellenic Council says, "I want someone who will look reasonably well twenty years afterward. I'm not interested in a striking beauty, but she must be a good cook. I want somebody who is not quite as smart as myself. As a one-word description of the girl, she must be 'substantial.'"

Charlie Turbyville, captain of the football team, admits his weakness for blonds of a reserved and intelligent type.

"She must be athletic, possibly go out for a little football now and then, and naturally she must root for Georgia," he says. He was firm in his stipulation that she must not smoke or drink.

"I want a raving beauty, and one that I can boss," says Hudson (Senator) Moore, campus leader. "She must have common sense, but she can't be a bookworm. I want a good sport." And when questioned as to her domestic qualifications he humorously adds, "I want a girl with enough money so I can hire a cook."

"I don't want a Mae West type, but I'm a firm believer in curves instead of corners," comments Lamar Kemp, transfer student from Oglethorpe University and former editor of the paper there. "I want a modern type with attractiveness plus personality. I am not averse to her smoking or indulging in an occasional cocktail. As for knowledge, she must be well versed on present-day subjects. She must have strong basic ideals together with the broad open-mindedness of today."

Graham Batchelor, former captain of the football team, is on the look-out for a small brunet. On the question of smoking, he says: "I see no reason to try to exclude women from a bad habit enjoyed so thoroughly by men.

"As for her drinking," he continues, "positively no. This subject should come under the head of common sense. The girl must have a certain degree of intelligence, but a genius is barred. Dancing should be of as much importance to women as athletics are to men."

Frazier Moore, graduate student of Atlanta, doesn't care for an unusually beautiful girl, but she must have a pleasing appearance and an intelligent face. "She will have to possess a good disposition to get along with me. I want a fairly intelligent woman, morals above reproach. She must be a lady in the drawing room, but she must know the way to the kitchen. The main thing is that she will have to root for me or make me think she does."

Webb (Stub) Norman, president of the Athletic Association, has an eye on brunets, easy to look at and easy to get along with. "She must be pleasingly plump, if you know what I mean, and since we've got to eat, she had better know how to cook." This characteristic statement sums up his ideal wife: She must be a neat little job."

Associate editor of the *Red and Black,* Hugh Lawson says:

"I want a woman whose capabilities are limitless, whose physical attributes are above par, who detests bridge with a passion, and who considers afternoon teas a vice."

All of which leads us to the natural conclusion that a century and a half have made no difference at all in what men demand of their ideal woman . . . and very little difference in what women demand of their ideal man.

1935

College Students View Marriage

Men Marry the Girl Who Hands Out the Keenest Line, Says One Co-Ed at the University of Georgia; and the Youngest Senior Merely Shrugs Away the Question of Matrimony.

Do college students favor matrimony, or does a diploma make a career seem more important?

Pretty co-eds and male students at the University of Georgia agree that college does do something to one's viewpoint, but not always the same thing.

For instance, Rae Neal, recently selected by the nationally known artist, McClelland Barclay, as the most beautiful girl at the university, feels that her ideas of marriage have grown more sensible during her co-ed days.

"I used to think of marriage as a sort of dream," she explains, "but now I can see it from more of a common-sense viewpoint. I am no longer looking for an ideal man, and I certainly don't expect to sit down and wait until Prince Charming comes along. What I want now is just a real man, and I can put up with his faults if he can put up with mine. I used to think, too, that a girl should expect to marry a man who could support her in such fashion that no effort was required on her part. I know now that if a girl really loves a man, she should be willing to do her part in everything."

These are Rae's ideas after having been thrown with men en masse in a large student body. The effect has been quite otherwise in the case of Howard Parks, from Newnan. Mixing with so many pretty co-eds has inspired him with the determination to remain footloose for some time to come. "College has given me a greater desire than ever to be a bachelor," he says. "There are too many attractive girls to settle down to one."

Agnes Jarnagin of Athens declares that she doesn't believe in all this business about equal rights. "College has changed my ideas about the sort of man I could be congenial with," she says, "but I still want a husband who will open car doors for me. Give me a little plain, old-fashioned chivalry on the side."

Nell Johnson, also of Athens, and president of the Women's Pan-Hellenic Council, says that college has given her a better idea of what marriage should mean, but that she wants to have a career, before marriage. "I believe that either a career or marriage is a full-time job," she says, "and I don't think it would be fair to a husband to expect him to put up with a sort of part-time wife."

Meta Shaw of Valdosta has ideas that run along parallel lines. "I used to want to be self-supporting," she smiled, "and had a lot of ideas about a career, but, well, maybe, I'm just meeting more interesting people now than I used to."

But Dorothy Verner of Commerce thinks that a wife who can make good outside the home brings more to matrimony than she would otherwise.

"I want more than a sack of flour and a pound of meat in my pantry before I take the fatal leap," she declares. "College has brought home to me the fact that these 'one-room flat' marriages don't always endure. Besides, with the economic situation so uncertain nowadays, it wouldn't be so bad to know that a wife could put her shoulder to the wheel if necessary."

Tom Dozier, editor of the *Red and Black*, agrees with Dorothy, that marriage has its practical side and that when the wolf knocks at the door, love often flees out of the window. "Marriage," he said, "therefore seems much farther away than when I donned my freshman cap. Having decided to be a newspaper man I realize that I have just about as much business thinking of getting married as a horse has of trying to trot along on roller skates. Still," he added, "like most other morons, I shall probably live to watch my common-sense views fade out in the incandescent radiance of some dizzy blond head."

Advice to a single woman: Hold an egg in your mouth. Then rush out into the yard. The first man you see will be your future husband.

—old-time Georgia superstition

Perry Hudson, who comes from Argentina, also takes a pessimistic view of the situation.

"Life is more reliable without marriage," he points out. Not only college but women in general have made me decide never to get married. Changeable women would ruin the dependable future that I desire most."

But Bill Hubbard of Rockmart editor of *Pandora,* is an optimist with a practical streak.

"College teaches you that you can't marry so soon," says Bill. "There wouldn't be enough money to support a wife properly. However," he adds triumphantly, "love will find a way."

Jasper Dorsey of Marietta, cadet colonel of the R.O.T.C. unit at the University of Georgia, is willing to take a chance on the high cost of matrimony.

"College," says Jasper, "has made me believe that you don't have to have a million dollars to get married." He went on to add that his attitude towards marriage has changed, but that his idea of the type of girl he prefers has not.

Dameron Black of Atlanta says that his ideas on marriage have altered enormously since he came to college. In his opinion, real education and a career should be the paramount ambition. Marriage, he thinks, will take care of itself.

Belle Meador, also of Atlanta, admits that college has given her a more practical view of men. "I used to think that I would go to college and find the perfect man. Now, I know there isn't any such animal."

Stub Norman, of Washington, Georgia, president of the Athletic Association, says that meeting various types of girls at college has given him a broader idea of what congenial companionship can mean. "Or," he added, "maybe it is just one girl who has taught me this. Anyway, I used to think I wanted the typical, old-fashioned, home-loving type. Now I know that I want somebody who will be on my own level, both intellectually and in business as well."

Cornelia MacIntyre, of Savannah, transfer student from Vassar, has her own ideas on the subject. "It is not the college influence that matters," she says, "but the men you meet."

Doris Malone, of Atlanta, wants a career at the present writing. "But," she said sagely, "if a girl falls in love with the right man, I certainly think she should marry him."

"College brings you to earth in a very decided manner, remarks Rachel Hamby of Atlanta. "You get down to business after you come to a place like this. But college also makes you much more independent, and you no longer feel that marriage is a necessity. There's so much else to do."

Marguerite Ferrand, French exchange student who comes to Georgia from the University of Paris, was more emphatic on the subject of careers.

"I've discovered there is no ideal man. I know them too well," she says. "I don't have the time to waste on marriage. College did not teach it, but marriage is a sentiment in which everybody loses everything and gains nothing. A career is far more important to me. But if a girl gets married and it doesn't work, it is still wise for her to have a career to depend on, for if she expects to be helped by a man she must help him."

Some of the co-eds demonstrated that college has taught them the value of a wisecrack.

Ida Mogul, associate editor of the *Red and Black*, says, "I'm cynical about some things but not about marriage. To me it represents the perfect union of two benighted souls who probably will change their minds in a few years.

"Marriage," concludes Ida, "is also a profit-making institution. Think of what the honeymoon trade means to Niagara Falls."

"I don't believe in love that is supposed to 'sweep you off your feet,'" declares Lucille Miller of Bainbridge, Georgia. "I used to, though. But now I know that when a man gets ready to marry he doesn't look for the one and only love of his life. He just marries the girl who has the keenest line handed out in the most casual fashion."

And some of the boys are still in a fog. DeNean Stafford, of Washington, D.C., president of the Pan-Hellenic Council says, "I came to the university perfectly nil and I suppose I will leave the same way." Mr. Stafford, of course, meant so far as the subject of girls is concerned. Asa Candler, of Atlanta, says that he hasn't given the subject much thought, but he does believe that it takes more than a little romance and a lot of wedding presents to make a happy marriage.

Stough Beers of Atlanta declares that college hasn't changed his ideas about wanting to get married, but has simply increased the number of girls he would like to share his future with. Right now he is trying to decide between three and is all confused.

But Andrew Cain, fifteen-year-old university senior who hails from Dahlonega, simply shrugs his shoulders and smiles when asked for his views on matrimony.

"Why, my dear young lady," he declares, "I've never had time to give the subject a thought."

1935

Find Someone to Love

Elberton's oldest living couple, Mr. and Mrs. James McIntosh, recently celebrated their fifty-ninth wedding anniversary. Only two of their six children are living, Mrs. A.F. Archer and John Hawes McIntosh, of Elberton. They have two grandchildren, Miss Mary Louise McIntosh and Mrs. John Leslie Baker, of Atlanta.

"My wife's fine cooking is the reason I'm living today," declared Mr. McIntosh, eighty-four years old and the second-oldest man in Elberton. "Why," he added, "her old-fashioned light bread and coffee would help keep anybody young."

With her thirty-five-year-old parrot on her shoulder, dainty and diminutive Mrs. McIntosh observed, "My love for life and people keeps me young. I attribute my long life, however, to providence. At eighty-two I am still young in spirit."

Blue-eyed Mrs. McIntosh, formerly Mary Jane Arnold, presented an unforgettable picture with her soft gray hair accented by her black dress and her wedding collar of old lace. Her wedding pin clasped at her throat and her wedding gloves served to revive old memories.

Declaring that he believed in love-at-first-sight romances, Mr. Mc-

Intosh said, "I fell in love with Mary Jane when I first saw her. I met her at a social one night and when she entered the room I knew she was my future wife."

Of their wedding day, they recalled that they were married at two o'clock in the old Arnold home in Elberton. Mr. McIntosh smiled and said, "We didn't go away on a honeymoon, but we did attend a grand reception at Heardmont after the wedding. Although Heardmont is only twelve miles from Elberton, it was night when we arrived. Remember, it was in the horse-and-buggy days and we thought we had gone quite a distance."

Still intensely active, Mrs. McIntosh takes care of her ten-room home. She does her own cooking and she finds time to crochet and embroider. Recently she won several prizes in needlework.

At one time Mr. McIntosh took an active part in civic affairs. He was county commissioner of roads and revenue for ten years, sheriff for ten years, and a member of the city council. For many years he was engaged in the mercantile business.

At present, Mr. McIntosh's chief source of exercise is walking. He enjoys long walks every day, and for relaxation there's nothing that suits him better than his pipe, which he smokes only after meals. On recalling a youthful escapade he chuckled, "I took one chew of tobacco at the age of twelve, but that was enough for a lifetime."

The great out-of-doors still appeals to them both. One of their chief interests lies in their azalea garden, which has the formosa, the famous Indica variety. During season the public is invited to visit their azaleas, known as the oldest in northeast Georgia.

Mr. and Mrs. McIntosh are convinced that the younger generation is no worse than any preceding generation. "We think they're all right," they agreed, "and with their added opportunities they get along better."

As the interview ended, Mr. McIntosh offered this sagacious bit of advice: "Find someone to love and stay in love."

"Yes," said Mrs. McIntosh, "and stay in love with life."

1941

Author's Note: Mr. and Mrs. McIntosh celebrated nine more anniversaries together, sixty-eight in all. They were the parents of the late John Hawes McIntosh, author of The Official History of Elbert County 1790–1935, Supplement 1935–1939, *published by Cherokee Publishing Company.*

Cold Feet

Ezra Green admitted he had never hit a lick of work and had no intentions of starting. For fear of doing something wrong, he decided to do nothing. He stopped playing checkers. He might make the wrong move.

He did not rush into matrimony. At sixty-nine, however, his caution seemed to diminish after Tom Boley died and left his widow Ezzie a chunk of worldly goods.

Reuben Adams asked for the truth. "Ezra," he inquired, "are you marrying for love or for money?"

"Now, Reuben," said Ezra, "you know I wouldn't let the root of all evil come between Ezzie and me."

On Ezra's wedding day Reuben followed the groom-to-be out of Bailey's Barber Shop. "Old boy, aren't you afraid you'll get cold feet?"

"No, Reuben, it's like this. My feet have been cold for a long time. And if I keep on waiting, complications *could* set in."

1975

Old Matt, a Short Story

Old Matt Tucker knew about life. Things did not uproot him. The day he proposed he said, "Drucilla, I want you permanent. I ain't expectin' too much of you and don't you go lookin' for too much in me." Drucilla smiled, and they were wed.

Sure they had their troubles. Their first child died. The second and third were deaf and mute. When friends came by to offer their consolation Matt said, "If it's to be, it be's."

The day of the Big Storm, Matt's roof sailed clear off. Neighbors ran down to Matt's cabin. They found him in the kitchen polishing his big black boots. Drucilla was stringing beans peaceful-like. Matt put down his boots and looked up toward a pine tree with its top twisted off. He observed, "'Pears to me there's a lot more sky with the roof blowed off."

Their fourth son was suspected of stealing chickens, but they believed in their boy. When the sheriff came calling, Matt said, "Sheriff, when I ask my boy somethin' he gives it to me straight. Anyway, I don't recollect havin' chicken for dinner lately."

Matt got riled with Tim Carter for making fun of his deaf and mute sons. He went into his garden and buried an old rusty knife. "When a man cuts my heart I try to bury my grudge. A garden won't grow if you're feudin' with your neighbor."

Matt was not acquainted with Achilles and least of all his heel, but like every living soul, he had one. His next-door neighbor, Letitia Belton, was a young widow who had apparently passed the mourning stage. When Matt worked in his garden, she would supply him with lemonade. "Just so you won't get overheated," she explained. The gardener had gumption enough to know that his neighbor's lemonade might lead to more than stomach colic, but the widow smiled sideways and kept on pouring.

One Sunday Letitia sashayed down the church aisle, and the preacher might as well have stopped for silent prayer. She took her seat directly across from Drucilla and Matt. Drucilla appeared to be listening to Brother Lindsey's sermon. Matt edged a glance across the aisle, and Letitia gentled a look toward him that made him feel right spry.

Brother Lindsey switched his message from the pains of the building fund to the woes of the sinner. He thumbed through his Bible and failed to find the exact admonition. Common sense rescued him and he advised, "Love thy neighbor but don't overdo it. Beware of a scheming woman whose husband has gone to his reward. Men, watch a woman who fishes for suckers. Suckers are blind to lures. Women, keep an eye on your mates, and be

The groom was clad in goosepimples and he wore a smile. The bride wore white.
—old edition of the *Elberton Star*

willing to forgive even if they stray a little. Remember, one time you thought they were right worthwhile."

Drucilla had sense enough to know that a man does not always head for home, and sometimes he might tilt his head sideways to get a better view of figures and shapes. In fact, she knew Matt like she knew Genesis. When his eyes started wandering too much, Drucilla cooked an apple pie that could out-tempt a sashaying woman.

When the widow's pipes busted in five degrees below zero, Matt vowed he was plumb good at fixing leaks under certain circumstances. Even though the water kept rising higher and higher, he was faithful in pursuing his task. In fact, he pursued his task long enough for the deacons to have a special called meeting. It appeared to Matt that sometimes deacons have a right smart skill in stirring up trouble.

Deacon Snellgrove droned over a tedious page of Matt's personal conduct. Matt sat in shelled silence and shielded his face with his right hand. He did not know that his wife had entered the church.

Deacon Betcherster cleared his throat and said, "Deacons, do you agree that Matt Tucker should be publicly scolded for his conduct?"

Drucilla stood up and said, "Not until you hear from me."

Deacon Snellgrove interposed. "But Drucilla, hasn't that widow woman just about broken up your home?"

Matt bent low and studied his knotted up shoelaces.

Drucilla countered with a question. "Was Letitia Belton at church Sunday?"

"Yes," answered Deacon Snellgrove.

"What did she wear?"

"A skirt that was way above where it ought to be," Deacon Seymour recollected.

"Deacon Betcherster, what color was her blouse? Was it thick or thin?"

"It was a purplish blue and pow'ful thin."

Drucilla stretched her shoulders toward Brasstown Bald. "Now tell me, Deacon Seymour, did you think Brother Lindsey preached a substantial sermon last Sunday?"

"Yes'm. He sure can keep you awake."

"What was his text?"

No answer.

Drucilla persisted. "Is there a deacon here tonight who can tell me what his text was?"

The deacons bowed their heads.

"Matt, do you remember one thing the preacher said last Sunday?"

"Yes," he recalled, he quoted a man named Socrates who said that the life which is unexamined is not worth living."

Drucilla smiled and looked at her mate. She remembered when he was young, tall, tuned to the plow, and straight as a Georgia pine in the sun.

Matt took a long look at his wife. She was as pretty as a pink forget-me-not. Her hair was soft and framed a face that looked like a woman should.

He stood up and took his wife by the hand and said, "Come, Drucilla, it's time for us to go home."

"Yes," she agreed, "and deacons, if you'll just listen to the preacher when he tells you about Socrates, you'll know a *good* man when you see one."

As they walked down the road, the fireflies seemed enchanted as they lit up their love lanterns all over the sky.

Words didn't roll out handy for Old Matt that night. But one thing he knew for sure. If there was anything that counted in this world, it was a faithful, lovin' woman.

Dear Mabel

Dear Mabel,

I won't be seeing George any more. Our engagement is broken. I'll miss him. You would too if he had been coming around for 47 years. I remember the first night he called. I was eating supper and he admired my biscuits. Since then he has dropped by three nights a week at supper time. That's a lot of biscuits.

Today I opened my hope chest and took out my wedding ring quilt and hung it in the sun. Do you know a good bleach for pillow cases, sheets and bureau runners? Mabel, I might as well be sensible and go on and use these things.

Everybody knows we tried to get married. We got our license and on the way to the preacher's house George started sneezing. I thought he'd never stop. He decided he was allergic to something. It seems strange but every time I mention matrimony he sneezes. Last night when I brought up the subject he pushed back his plate and said he'd better cut down on starches.

Mabel, I'm absolutely, positively through with George. Well, I've got biscuits in the oven and there's someone at the door. Be seeing you.

Love,

Sadie

P. S. Mabel, it's George and you know he's just the dearest thing. Today's my birthday and he brought me a five-pound sack of flour.

* * *

Dear Mabel,

Yesterday I went to the doctor and a strange thing happened. I got out my list of ailments and the minute I got to the third page of my problems, my doctor started shivering. He took two pills and bowed his head. Mabel, I couldn't help but hope he might have been praying for me. But when he put his hand over his heart I felt obligated to take his pulse. Mabel, I do believe he ought to see *his* doctor.

I have almost decided I will look for another doctor. Do you know that the last time I was in the hospital my doctor came to see me but he just stood in the doorway? Who wants a doctor who starts running the minute you reach for your list! Doctors are so different today. Why, they used to sit on my bed and hold my hand. One or two even kissed my brow, and Mabel, you know as well as I do that a little understanding goes a *long* way.

Oh Mabel, how this world has changed! One thing I know for sure. It has changed too much for me.

Love,
Sadie

P. S. Dear Mabel, I have big news for you. I don't see why my doctor left the medical profession but he did. He's working for the IRS. I'm glad that now I have someone to advise me what to withhold and what to confess.

* * *

Dear Mabel,

You are so good to mail me the article on *The Fear of Flying* that was published in the *People's Dilemma Magazine*. But you mailed it too late.

Last week I received an invitation to be the guest of Delta on a plane trip around the city of Atlanta. Miss Cash, my principal, insisted on my going. She seemed to feel that I needed to reach a higher elevation. When she came by to go to the airport I backed out. I said, "Miss Cash, I can't go. I've always known that if I flew, I would crash. To fly is to say goodbye."

But Mabel, wait now. Don't sit down. You'd better lie down when I tell you what George, the man that I've cooked biscuits for every day for forty years, had the nerve to say, "Please go."

That was enough. I went. As we soared over Stone Mountain Miss Cash said, "Isn't this heavenly!" With a celestial prayer between Stone Mountain and Kennesaw Mountain I begged, "Please, Miss Cash, don't rush my destination."

I could not believe it when I landed safely. But oh, Mabel, when I landed, I knew my life would never be the same. To *think* that George insisted that I fly when I said plainly that it would be goodbye forever. I keep hearing him say, "Oh, go on. Go on." And I see that look of secret hope in his eyes.

Now that I have flown one time, George seems more and more interested in my getting off the ground and getting up in the air. But can you be up in the air and on shaky ground all at the same time? I don't know, Mabel, I just don't know.

Love,
Sadie

* * *

Dear Mabel,

All these years I have come to you with my problems. How could I ever do without you!

The other night I overheard my mother-in-law tell George that when Sadie cooks spaghetti you'll never forget it. I was plumb overjoyed to hear it. I do believe that is the highest compliment she has ever paid me.

Well, that sent me steaming to the kitchen. Since my spaghetti was so good I decided to invite my neighbors in for supper. I livened up my recipe with a little more garlic and red pepper. And at the last minute I added a sizable amount of horseradish so *everybody* could breathe easy.

So far I haven't heard from my neighbors, but Mabel, for some unknown reason my dear darling George developed a severe condition. It hurt

me right deep when he said, "Sadie, that's the last spaghetti I will ever eat."
And Mabel—it was!

Oh Mabel, if *only* I had poached him an egg!
> Love,
> Sadie

* * *

Dear Mabel,

You remember I told you how happy I was when I overheard my mother-in-law tell George that when you eat Sadie's spaghetti you'll never forget it. I took it as a compliment until I read your letter.

I'm glad you told me the truth even if it did hurt. You said that my mother-in-law told you that when you eat Sadie's spaghetti you'll regret it, that is, *if* you live to regret it. Much as I hate to admit it she was right. Look what happened to my dear darling George.

Mabel, please tell me what to do. Should I just turn a deaf ear or get a hearing aid? Or should I just stay out of the kitchen?
> Love,
> Sadie

P. S. I'm in a hurry to go to the grocery store. They're having a right good sale on extra-lean ground beef. Three whole pounds for one dollar.

Early Days of Elbert County

Having a knowledge of the history of where you live just makes the life you are living now that much more interesting and enjoyable.

—*Franklin Miller Garrett*

Asa Chandler's Diary

A diary kept in the 1800s by Asa Chandler, Elbert County minister, was found several years ago by Lois and Rod Daniel of Elberton. When they began remodeling their home on Tusten Street they found the diary stowed away in the loft.

Asa Chandler was the sixth child of Joseph Chandler and Sara Farmer Chandler of North Carolina and Franklin County, Georgia. He was born in Franklin County August 22, 1808. He attended Ruckersville Academy and at the age of fourteen he joined the Baptist Church of Poplar Springs in Franklin County. He preached his first sermon at sixteen and, at twenty-one, was ordained as a Baptist minister at Van's Creek Baptist Church in Ruckersville, Georgia. Chandler was minister of the First Baptist Church in Elberton, and he served many rural Baptist congregations in Northeast Georgia. He was moderator of the Sarepta Association from 1841 to 1873. He was married three times and had nine children. He died in 1874 at age sixty-six.

The diary is a short journal that gives a report of his travels as a minister. Chandler wrote a short autobiographical sketch, and at the end he listed the persons he had baptized and married. Primary places mentioned were Elbert, Bibb, Franklin, Green, Hall, Lumpkin, and Richmond counties, as well as South Carolina.

The hardship and struggles of a circuit-rider preacher are evident in this diary. After the loss of his first wife and two daughters he wrote his sister on January 13, 1836: I hope the three of my family that are gone are now rejoicing with the blessed in heaven, while I am left to suffer his righteous will a while in this poor unfriendly world.

Chandler wrote that as he recovered from a fever he was "taken with a burning heat in his feet, supposed to be the fever leaving this family." His illness left him unable to walk for several months, and when he resumed preaching he had to preach sitting down, since he was unable to stand and walk for some time.

April 20, 1838

Left home with my wife and little daughter. Traveled 25 mi. to Monroe Walton County put up with Brother James Brown Sat. Sun. and Monday. Attended the Convention on Sunday. Heard Brethren Mercer, Posey and Mallory preach.

April 1839

Traveled for Sarepta Assoc. to be held at Black's Creek Madison County traveled till near night tried out a house to get lodging and was refused. Traveled 9 miles after night tried out seven houses and was refused admittance. Had thought of lying out was overtaken by a young Bro. Williams who took me to his father's Br. Dawson Williams.

Feb. 1841

Visited Rev. Dozier Thornton the oldest minister in this section of country. Supposed to be about 90.

In December 1844 Asa Chandler and the Reverend Peter Butler spent the night in Augusta. The Democrats were celebrating with parades and fireworks the victory of James Knox Polk, the eleventh president of the United States. Chandler wrote that amid all the excitement and celebration "we read the Bible and invoked God's blessing on our nation."

Beverly Allen Plantation

Everett Saggus

Beverly Allen Plantation has carved out a particular place in Georgia history, since it is one of the oldest plantations in the state and is one of the first taverns in North Georgia. Built in one year, 1783–1784, it is located high on a hill on Beaverdam Creek several miles above the town of old Petersburg in Elbert County.

The plantation was the home of William Allen, a merchant, who with his half brother Beverly Allen, a Methodist minister, emigrated from Virginia to Georgia soon after the Revolutionary War. The brothers were both Revolutionary War soldiers.

If Louise Wray Brown (Mrs. Chandler Brown, Sr.), well-known artist and owner of the plantation for more than forty years, had not persisted in having it placed on the National Register of Historic Places, it may well have been destroyed. As a result of the Richard B. Russell Dam and Lake Project, one side of the home is 200 feet from the water, and the other side of the home is only 130 feet from the water's edge.

According to Mrs. Brown, an authority on Elbert County history, the home is of heart pine with the framework twelve by twelve, put together with big wooden pegs. The two back rooms of the house, the kitchen and dining room, are the oldest and still have H and L hinges on the doors. Locks on the doors of the two back rooms, as well as the later additions, have the big Williamsburg type locks and Indian bars for extra protection.

The kitchen and dining room in the rear of the house have remained largely intact. The kitchen fireplace has been blocked and the mantel removed, but the wainscoting and chair rail remain. Evidences of late eighteenth- and early nineteenth-century designs are shown by the panelled wainscoting, chair rail, and porch door with H and L hinges.

The dining-room mantel has a simple trim that frames the fireplace opening and a narrow shelf detailed with a repeating circle and dentil motif. Almost all the windows in this area and the later additions are nine-over-nine sash windows.

In 1803 the front part of the house was added by William Allen's son Beverly, for whom the plantation was named. Only the main house, a sixty-foot-deep well, now bricked up, and the Allen family cemetery remain. Records show that there were more structures that included a log storehouse, smoke house, slave quarters, and a carriage house. There were two hundred slaves on the two-thousand-acre plantation.

In the later addition of the home, a William Carpenter lock imported from England is on the parlor door, and on all the other doors. They have large keys with small brass doorknobs. The doors throughout the home are

Ghosts come calling at Beverly Allen Plantation, where stories of buried treasure and scars made by the boots of Yankee intruders have made life interesting for owners Mr. and Mrs. Chandler Brown. The home was built around 1784 by William Allen, who, with his brother Beverly, came from Virginia soon after the Revolution.

Crusader doors. The molding is in the form of a cross, and the lower part of the door is like an open Bible.

In Mrs. Brown's continuous research, she has found that at one time there was an incorporated town called Beverly. In 1790 the first district of Elbert County was laid off by William Allen's road, which extended from Cherokee Shoals on the Savannah River to Fishdam Ford on Broad River.

In the early 1800s William Allen's son Beverly applied for a tavern license in Elbert County. The license cost four hundred dollars a year. The stagecoach from Augusta made an overnight stop at the plantation. This stop gave the horses an opportunity to rest. Food and lodging cost travelers twenty-five cents per night. It cost much more to feed horses than humans.

During the War Between the States the Yankee raiders invaded the Allen home. They shot in the side door, kicked the front door open, and broke the lock. The print of the hobnailed boots is still on the front door.

When the Yankees found little sacks of starch instead of gold, they held a pistol to Mrs. Beverly Allen's head and tried to force her to give them all the money she had. Mrs. Allen, the former Mildred Henry, stood her ground and said, "Would you treat your poor mother like this?" They ransacked the house, but she never told them where the gold was hidden. It was in a secret drawer of her dresser.

It is still believed that there is gold on the plantation. The hidden gold is said to be worth more than a million dollars today. Over the years the acres surrounding the plantation have been dug up by scores of treasure hunters. Understandably Louise Brown never has any difficulty in getting someone to work in her flower garden, plow up a field, or whatever. She says beyond a doubt it is the most *dug-up* place in Elbert County. So is the old Allen cemetery, where gold is also believed to be buried. Wishful diggers, some with metal detectors, have left their mark in the never-ending search for the hidden treasure.

A variety of conjectures livens the search. Could the gold be under the ancient crape myrtle trees brought over in 1783–1784 from France to Charleston, South Carolina, and on to Elbert County? Could it be under the cedars or the old walnut tree? Is it hidden in one of the fireplaces or one of the chimneys? Is it under rocks in the flower garden? In the old burying ground? Under the walk? Down in the well? Or in the sunset each day?

"To me," says Louise Brown, "the sunset is worth all the gold."

The Allen home is not without its ghosts. In one of the oldest rooms in the house is a Seth Thomas clock on the mantel. "Sometimes the door to the clock opens, and the clock does strange things," said Mrs. Brown. "The day my granddaughter Connie Brown married in the formal garden, I noticed that the hands of the clock had moved to the precise hour of the wedding. The clock had not been wound in fifteen years. I had the pendulum taken off because it made so much noise. This is not the only peculiar phenomenon. When two of my relatives died, the hands of the clock moved to the hour that each one died."

No one can explain why a doorknob turns in the dining room and the door slowly opens, or why two family pets refuse to enter the kitchen. Rue, a little Chihuahua, and Mathilde, a Great Dane, cannot be coaxed to cross the kitchen threshold. They just bristle and shiver.

At times Louise Brown hears the sound of a hand rippling through water, back and forth. "Maybe it's Beverly Allen washing his hands," she suggested. "I do not panic when I hear a metaphysical guest climb the stairs and open and close doors.

"You have to have a second sight to see ghosts, but I must admit, however, that I do find comfort in ghosts. They are the real owners of Beverly Allen Plantation, together with the bees. I give in to the ghosts' whims. If a mug filled with coffee disappears, I'm not surprised. Perhaps ghosts get thirsty, too.

"There is no piano in the parlor any more, but sometimes when everything is quiet, I can hear my musically inclined ghost playing the piano. And the way the bees swarm around here they must hear the music too. They certainly have attended the garden weddings of my grandchildren. Wedding music stirs them up."

Several years ago one of Mrs. Brown's grandsons, Chandler, III, took pictures of the parlor. In one of the pictures of a mirror above the mantel was a reflection of a man wearing a white wig. Mrs. Brown said, "Maybe that's Beverly Allen."

The grandson asked, "But what about this other little face? Who is he?"

They did not need extrasensory perception to see the tiny face of a red-headed Irishman.

When William Allen's son Beverly was at the point of death, he called his half brother, Singleton Allen, and he took three keys off his neck and gave them to Singleton. Some years ago when the Allen home was painted and repairs were made, three keys were found under the rock of one of the chimneys. The mystery of the keys remains unsolved. The keys are now hanging on the wall of the old kitchen. Another unsolved mystery is the grave under the parlor. The grave was discovered several years ago when the front porch was repaired.

Whatever the reason—love for history, quest for gold, excitement of ghosts—Beverly Allen Plantation has a constant flow of visitors, students of all ages, professors, adult groups, friends, relatives, and history buffs. On the wall of the front porch there is a friendly bit of verse that matches the warmth of Louise Brown's welcome:

Give this house oh traveler pray
A blessing as you pass this way
And if you've time, I beg your pardon,
While you're at it—bless the garden.

The Early Days of Elbert County

When a man is thirsty, he searches for a trickle of water. But when he finds an abundant spring, it is time to call a halt and say, "*This is a place for living.*" Tradition says that William Woodley and a small number of settlers found such a place. Why go on when the spring flowed deep and clear?

So, far into the hills of Northeast Georgia a village was born. The story is told that William Woodley built the first home near the Old Town Springs. Two or three other families also stayed. This was about 1769. No records show from what place Woodley came or where he moved after he left the Old Town Springs. Tradition also says that a small group of settlers had come even before 1769. The Old Town Springs later became known as Elberton.

Elbert County was created by the Georgia State Legislature December 10, 1790, from part of Wilkes County which had included lands formerly ceded by the Cherokees and Creeks in 1773. It was named for Samuel Elbert, noted general in the Revolutionary War. After Elbert County was cut off from Wilkes County in 1790, three justices were appointed to select a site for the county court house. One of the justices was Stephen Heard, governor of Georgia in 1780. He came from Wilkes County on horseback.

The justices selected the present town of Elberton as a place for the court house. In its beginning Elberton was known as Elbertville. After the court house and jail were built the town was called Elbert County Court House. Elberton was incorporated in 1803 with a legislative act that began: 'Whereas the town of Elberton needs regulating.' So five commissioners were appointed to regulate and rule the town: Middle Woods, Reuben Lindsey, Dr. John T. Gilmer, Beckham Dye, and James Alston.

Forgotten Towns of Elbert County

Petersburg—once Georgia's third largest city—lies beneath the waters of Clark Hill Reservoir. Fort James and Dartmouth, like Petersburg, are forgotten towns of Georgia.

Fort James, situated on a point of land between the Broad and the Savannah Rivers, was built to defend the old Colonial settlement at Dartmouth. History tells us that Fort James, which protected the settlers from attacks by the Creeks and Cherokees, was a four-square stockade with "salient bastions at each angle, surmounted by a blockhouse and guarded by a number of swivel guns. The stockade was an acre in extent. Within it was a house for the commandant, quarters for the various officers and barracks for the garrison. The entire force consisted of fifty rangers, each of them well mounted and armed."

The first town to be established in Elbert County was Dartmouth. After 1789 a group of Virginians settled in the Broad River country and named their town, Dartmouth, for the town in Virginia. It had the distinction of being the third town to be established in Georgia. Dartmouth at one time had a population of about three hundred but Dartmouth and Fort James vanished after several years. Dartmouth soon gave way to Petersburg. Dionysius Oliver, one of the pioneer settlers, is said to have named Petersburg for his native home in Virginia.

To the historian, Petersburg is more than just an old forgotten tobacco market. At one time it became the great tobacco center of the district with a population of more than a thousand. Many wealthy Virginians settled on Broad River and acquired the valuable lands in the Savannah Valley. Petersburg became an active, wealthy center as well as a powerful political center. It had two newspapers. The tobacco, packed in large hogsheads, was shipped by flatboat to Augusta and Savannah where it was sent directly to England. Petersburg merchants were both exporters and importers, and Petersburg prospered because goods were sold much more cheaply there than in Augusta.

One descendant of an old Petersburg family recalled stories told him of the exciting day when the "river was up" and there was much fear for the safety of those who made trips on the flatboats. During extremely high tide the trip to Augusta was made in less than a day, but the trip back often took more than a week. One incident was recalled when Broad River was so swollen that the flatboats reached Augusta in much less than a day, a distance of about sixty miles, and Augusta itself was so flooded that these same flatboats floated up Broad Street.

One person who lived in the community recalls stories handed down to him. He said, "When the flatboats got back safely after high waters, Petersburg was jubilant. There would be long tables of food in the big houses and much rejoicing."

According to stories told, bonfires seemed to be a favorite pastime for the young and old, and, about dusk, crowds would gather. Rich mingled with poor, and many tales of old Virginia were exchanged. The graceful Virginia reel was put to test but according to the old timers, the old-fashioned square dance was even more popular.

According to Dr. E. Merton Coulter, historian, Petersburg was a wealthy place. In the old deed files of Elbert County he found recorded the sale of city lots for as much as $1,200 each.

Petersburg's fame was short lived, however. One historian succinctly records its end: "Tobacco gave way in the first decade of the new century, and Petersburg began to decline. With the coming of the steamboats and the abandonment of tobacco planting and the growth of Augusta, its decay was rapid, and now not one house remains."

Petersburg can be remembered, however, for many reasons. It was the fourth town to be established in Georgia. It bears the distinction of having two United States senators serving in Congress at the same time. They were Judge Charles Tait and Dr. William Wyatt Bibb, for whom Bibb County is named. Later Bibb moved to Alabama and he became the first territorial governor of Alabama. Tait moved to Alabama also and he became the first federal judge of the Alabama territory.

The first cotton factory and the first tobacco warehouse in the south were in Petersburg. The first four-wheel vehicle ever brought into the state is said to have been brought to Petersburg by John M. White.

According to McIntosh's *Elbert County History*, most of the people in Petersburg were Virginians and they organized a "society for the betterment of social, educational and industrial advancement." They realized the urgent need for a school so the Petersburg Academy was established. This society in Petersburg gave to John Smithson the idea of his gift to the government, which later became the Smithsonian Institution in Washington, D.C.

Ruckersville and Georgia's First Millionaire

On Van's Creek near an old Indian trail is Ruckersville, settled in 1773 by Virginia aristocrats who moved in to take up land grants—the first being taken by John Rucker and John White.

In 1822 the village of Ruckersville was incorporated, taking its name from Ruckersville, Virginia. In 1827 Sherwood's *Gazeteer* described it as having ten houses, six stores and shops, an academy and a house of worship for the Baptists. Later it became a thriving town of six or seven hundred people, fifty stores, a newspaper, two banks, and two schools. A Princeton graduate was the principal of its academy, and it is credited with producing Georgia's first millionaire, Joseph Rucker.

Joseph was the son of John and Elizabeth Tinsley Rucker, and in 1812 he married Margaret Houston Speer, daughter of William Speer, who lived at Cherokee Falls on the Savannah River, and they established their home in Ruckersville.

The land was young, the roads were bad, from Ruckersville to Augusta was a four-day trip, and yet in that secluded locality, remote from mart, and market, Joseph Rucker created a fortune great for his day and generation.

Joseph Rucker must have been an organizer for there was much to be done. He had sawmills, his own tanyard and tanners, harness makers and shoemakers, and mills to convert grain into flour and meal. There were the necessary blacksmiths, wheelwrights, and carpenters. Not only was there cotton to be ginned but there was cloth to be woven. Cotton was shipped in Petersburg boats down the Savannah River to Augusta.

According to the *Cyclopedia of Georgia,* Joseph Rucker showed kindness and justice in his treatment of his slaves. "There were slaves who were trained and taught and how humanely and well this was done is shown by the conduct of those same slaves when, during the war, discipline was necessarily relaxed and control partially suspended."

The late James S. Lamar, of Augusta, son-in-law of Joseph Rucker, once wrote of his father-in-law's visits to Elberton: "It was his custom to go to Elberton on the first Tuesday in every month, when the principal men of the county would assemble in a sort of general meeting together, to attend the sheriff sales, to transact business with each other, to laugh and talk and crack jokes, and especially to save the country by discussing politics. During court week he would often meet with Alexander Stephens and Robert Toombs."

Georgia's first millionaire was organizer, president, cashier, and stockholder of the Bank of Ruckersville. In fact he was the bank. It must have been a strange sight to see a bank surrounded by a forest. It was a small, nondescript frame building. "Its doors and shutters were studded with nails at close and regular intervals to guard against the burglars' axe. It had a safe without a time lock, opened with a key carried by the president." The Bank of Ruckersville became nationally known and any business transaction involving it was honored throughout the United States. Corra Harris once wrote that her grandfather, John M. White, transported $150,000 in currency in the foot of his buggy from Milledgeville, the capital, to Ruckersville, and deposited it there for the state.

James Rucker, cousin of Joseph Rucker, also had a bank in Ruckersville. He had his bank in his house and the safe in which the money was placed was sold a number of years ago as junk. It served its last bit of usefulness at the old Rucker home as a hen's nest.

Rucker was not a doctor but he must have attended the sick as this old bill indicates:

2 visits attendance on your family	$1.56
Stomach Liquid	.20
Elixir and 1 visit	.89
Liquid Lavenders	.12

Joseph Rucker, whose family founded the village of Ruckersville, owned numerous businesses in the area and was president of the Bank of Ruckersville. Rucker is believed to be Georgia's first millionaire.

Laxative .... .20

Visits and 6 doses of medicine 1.16

The home of Joseph Rucker still stands today. Once the scene of hospitality and quiet elegance, it now waits and longs for restorative hands. Joseph and Margaret Rucker lie sleeping in the old graveyard at Van's Creek.

How Mammy Kate Rescued Stephen Heard

Elbert County is proud of Stephen Heard, governor of Georgia in 1780. He served under General Washington in the French and Indian wars. During the Battle of Kettle Creek he was captured by the British and sentenced to die. But Mammy Kate, a house slave belonging to Governor Heard, was determined to save her master. Her ingenuity is recorded in McIntosh's *Elbert County History*.

"One morning Mammy Kate, who measured over six feet, went to the fort and asked the soldier on duty to let her get her master's soiled linen. On her head was a large covered basket. The guard allowed her entrance into the cell. Governor Heard undoubtedly was grateful for his small stature. He soon found himself in the basket, covered with clothing. Mammy Kate placed the basket on her head and walked past the guard and a number of British officers. The night before she had brought two of Stephen's Arabian horses, Lightfoot and Silverheels, to the edge of Augusta and left them with a friend of Governor Heard. So Mammy Kate took her master to the place where the horses were. She leisurely made her way to the place of concealment where they mounted the horses and galloped away."

As they travelled toward home Stephen Heard promised to give Mammy Kate her freedom.

"Na, Marse Stephen," she answered, "You may set me free, but I ain't gwina set you free!"

Mammy Kate received her freedom, a deed to a small tract of land and a house, but she kept her promise and remained with the Heard family as long as she lived. On her deathbed she gave each of Stephen Heard's children one of her own. She lies buried in the corner of the Heard, Allen, McIntosh, Mattox burial ground at Heardmont. A large marker has been placed there in honor of this brave woman.

Elberton Academies

In 1826 the legislature incorporated the Elberton Female Academy, the state's second incorporated female school. According to Knight's *Landmarks, Memorials and Legends* the first female academy under state patronage was chartered at Harmony Grove in Jackson County in 1824, but it soon closed. Wesleyan College was not founded until after these dates, but it was the first school to confer a degree on a woman.

Legislative acts incorporated Philomathia Academy in 1823 and Eudisco Academy in 1823. Later the Elberton Male Academy was established.

Taxes Were Low

According to Mrs. Joseph T. Livsey of East Point, Governor Carl Sanders' great-great grandfather, Captain G. W. Harmon, once lived in Elberton. He had a large tannery. Since Captain Harmon was the grandfather of

Mrs. Livsey's husband, she has some of his valuable old records and account books.

John Billups bought 9½ pounds of beef at 4¢ a pound. His total meat bill was 42¢. John Moore bought 16½ pounds of beef for 66¢. Captain Harmon evidently felt pleased over his financial status from a personal observation written at the bottom of one of the account pages:

"A GREAT BUSINESS indeed for the year 1833."

Taxes in Elberton were not outrageously high in 1873. In a letter to Mr. Harmon this fact is brought out:

Dear Sir:

Yours of the 11th inst. at hand, and enclosed find three dollars. The Tax Collector will be in town tomorrow. I will settle your tax for you, your tax (2.50). I will hand you the change when you come down.

Yours respectfully,
James A. Andrew, Elberton

Old Globe Hotel

Elberton's first hotel, the Old Globe, stood on the site of the present Court House. According to records provided by Margaret Heard Dohme, the Globe was "an old inn" in 1835. The material and method of construction suggest that it could have been built in George Washington's administration. It was a large two-story building with green shutters and a gray shingled roof.

Until 1878, when the Elberton Airline Railroad was built from Toccoa to Elberton, the main contact with the outside world was the stage coach line between Elberton and Lexington. On reaching the Globe, the driver gave three strong blasts on his horn and people came or sent for their mail.

In early days the rates at the Globe as fixed by the Federal Court were: Dinner 31½ cents; Breakfast 25 cents; Supper 25 cents—Order of 1803. Lodging 12½ cents, Stable 12½ cents; Corn and Oats 12½ cents per gallon; Fodder per Bundle 3 cents.

The Globe was the mecca for political and social gatherings. Alexander Stephens and Robert Toombs were frequent guests. Those living at the Globe included bachelors, and widowers. Newlyweds also stayed there until their homes could be built.

H. C. Edmunds, a pharmacist, bought much of the material of the Globe when it was demolished in 1893, and he used it in building his new home and inn. This was later called the Commercial Hotel. The building is still standing on North Oliver Street.

1965

Many Noted People Have Visited Elberton

If all the great people who have planted their feet on Elbert County soil could return, many voices would ring out loud and clear. There would be Sam Rayburn who said, "This is a good town. Good people live here. They have served their country well. It gave us a man like Congressman Paul Brown, a great American and faithful servant of the people." Mr. Rayburn came to Elberton to celebrate Paul Brown Day in October 1955.

Alexander Stephens, vice president of the Confederacy, was a frequent visitor to Elberton. Once when he was making a speech at the court house square a heckler laughed at his small, frail body. He jeered, "If you were greased I could swallow you with one swallow." Stephens replied, "Then you'd have more brains in your belly than in your head."

Mrs. C. L. Dohme, the former Margaret Heard, Elberton historian, recalls stories told by her grandfather, James Lawrence Heard, descendant of Stephen Heard. Alexander Stephens often visited her grandfather. His bodyservant not only accompanied him on his trips but he hovered near him all the time. At the table he would stand back of Stephens' chair and look critically at everything on his master's plate. The servant would often say, "You don't want that, Mr. Stephens. Don't eat it." And Mr. Stephens did as he was told.

Mrs. Dohme recalls another Stephens visit: "One day when Stephens was dining with my father's family, my father's sister, Nancy Middleton Heard, was busy chattering away. Stephens said, 'Children should be seen and not heard.'

"Nancy replied, 'But I can't help being *Heard*.' Later he wrote Nancy and sent her a picture which she prized as one of her most cherished mementoes."

Colorful and hot-tempered Robert Toombs, famous Confederate orator and Confederate general, was a frequent visitor in Elberton. He often had dinner with William Harper Heard at the Old Globe Hotel, and the two talked many hours on the affairs of state.

Elbertonians have not forgotten the day in the 1920s when Marshall Foch came to Elberton. School officially closed, and although there may have been some students who could not sing all verses of *The Star Spangled Banner*, there were very few students throughout the crowd who did not know *La Marseillaise*, the French national anthem. Foch smiled his victory smile when a great chorus of voices welcomed him.

William Jennings Bryan, who ran for president in three separate presidential campaigns, came to Elberton a number of times. The last speech he made here was at the First Methodist Church.

Red-haired, fiery Tom Watson gave Elberton a spark as he spoke in defense of the little farmer, both white and black. His great oratorical ability earned for him the title, "The Patrick Henry of Georgia Farmers."

Corra Harris, who was born and reared in Elbert County, revisited Elberton in later years. Once when she talked to the students of Elberton Public School, she paid her native birthplace a great compliment: "These hills and valleys I love. The life that I have known and the people I have known are my plots. My forebears knew adversity and they were not felled. These are my own." Her most popular book, *A Circuit Rider's Wife*, was made into a movie, *I'd Climb the Highest Mountain*. Other books included: *Eve's Second Husband*, *As A Woman Thinks*, and *Happy Pilgrimage*. She was also a longtime columnist for the *Atlanta Journal* and a regular contributor to the *Saturday Evening Post*.

Magnolia Plantation

On Magnolia Plantation in the little town of Danville live two women who are surrounded by priceless heirlooms. They cherish the memories of the past, but they are vitally aware of the present and have great hopes for the future. They are eighty-eight-year-old Miss Henrietta Louise Hughes and her sister-in-law, two years her junior, Mrs. Hugh Dennard Hughes, the former Miss Agnes Goss of Athens.

Known to their friends and neighbors as Miss Hennilu and Miss Agnes, they live in a classic white plantation house surrounded by huge magnolias. A white picket fence neatly encloses the front yard that glistens with hard-packed white sand and not a blade of grass. Beyond the fence are lawns of grass and plantings of rare and exotic shrubs, camellias, and more than thirty varieties of azaleas.

Along the front porch are rocking chairs, some more than a hundred years old, with footrests for really relaxed rocking. It is perfectly apparent to anyone who sees this house in its beautiful setting that it has long been a home deeply loved and carefully kept.

This was the home of Miss Henrietta's parents, the late Dudley Mays and Mary Dennard Hughes, and it was here on a plantation of more than a thousand acres that she grew up with her two brothers, Hugh Dennard and Daniel. She loved it. In fact, she never wanted to leave home. The two years she spent at Lucy Cobb Institute in Athens (where she was a classmate of Miss Agnes, who married her brother and now shares the ancestral home with her) and the two years spent at Georgia Normal Industrial College in Milledgeville were the most homesick days of her life. "At college I had high fevers but at home I quickly recovered," she recalled with a smile. "There were talks of a finishing school in Baltimore, but my fever mounted. When my parents finally decided to let me stay at home I got well and have been ever since. I love this ground and I have always wanted to put my feet down on it for good."

Yet, loving it with all her heart, she and her sister-in-law recently sold a thousand acres of their land for one purpose and one purpose only—to build a chapel at the State Future Farmers of America and Future Home-makers of America Camp on the shores of Lake Jackson, twelve miles from Covington, as a memorial to Dudley and Mary Hughes.

Dudley Hughes is best remembered in Georgia and throughout the country as the co-author of the National Vocational Education Act of 1917, which provided aid for vocational education in the public schools for youth and adults. He was also one of the builders and president of the Macon, Dublin and Savannah Railroad.

In the early days of their marriage, Dudley and Mary Hughes had recognized the needs of the people in their area, and in visiting the homes of impoverished farmers, they came to grips with want and the abyss of ignorance. Dudley Hughes walked over the farms and saw the desperate condition of those who tilled the soil in the only way they knew. He looked into the eyes of the boys whose only hope lay in the self-same cotton fields of their parents. These boys had never gone to school and had no thought of going.

Mary Hughes asked the mothers to bring their children to Sunday School but the mothers made no promises. In a little log church on Sunday morning she waited for folks who failed to come. One visit to a home was revealing. "We are poor, but we are proud," said one of the women. "We ain't sendin' our children because we don't have no way to pay our part."

"Yes, you do," said Mary Hughes. "You have chickens, don't you?"

"Yes'm."

"Well, then, each child who comes can bring an egg. When roll is called he'll stand and say, 'John Smith, present, with an egg.' Then my husband will buy or sell the eggs to get what is needed for the Sunday School."

This worked. Mrs. Hughes was the organist and her husband was the superintendent. They began to teach the young ones, and later on the older ones, to read and write. They taught them to read simple Bible verses, and it was a great day when they recognized their own names in print. Courses varied according to the needs of the people. Besides the three R's, there were lessons in good manners, grooming and dressmaking.

Now Mt. Zion Missionary Baptist Church with a membership of about two hundred is the result of the Wee Egg Sunday School. There is a minister's study, a pastorium, and a new Sunday School annex, recently dedicated in memory of Mr. and Mrs. Hughes. At Mercer University in Macon a lasting tribute stands: the Mary Dennard Hughes Christian Scholarship presented by the Woman's Missionary Union of the Ebenezer Baptist Association.

Perhaps no man in America understood the needs of the people more than Dudley Hughes. When he was elected to Congress, he went to work on legislation for vocational education. His wife was often by his side and reminding him to *remember the girls. Don't leave out the homemakers.* Congressman Hughes got his bill through the House, and his collaborator, Georgia's Senator Hoke Smith, steered it through the Senate, giving our country one of its most important and rewarding gifts, vocational education. From the interest Mary Hughes showed in promoting this bill, she received the title of Mother of FHA, and in 1952 she was given honorary membership by the National Association of FHA.

Few people could match Mrs. Hughes' talents. She was an excellent horsewoman, pianist, organist, and an accomplished artist and singer. At Magnolia Plantation are many of her oil paintings. She was adept in French embroidery, and one mantel is graced by a triple mirror in frames that she carved. Her husband often said that when man's mind is trained and his hand left unskilled, he is only half-educated. Dudley Hughes had reason to be proud of his talented wife and the versatility of her hands.

During Mr. Hughes' congressional years, Mrs. Hughes led an exciting life in the political and social circles of Washington. She knew personally nine presidents, the two Roosevelts, Hoover, Coolidge, Harding, Wilson, Taft, McKinley, and Grant.

No less exciting today is the life of Miss Henrietta and Miss Agnes. One Danville resident said of the sisters, "They are the two busiest ladies in Twiggs County." Miss Henrietta is a deacon at Danville Baptist Church. "I do my share of expatiating to the brethren, and what I say gives them food for thought," she said with a sly twinkle. "I was reared on a church bench.

When I was an infant my parents would stretch me out on a bench and I am sure I slept through many a sermon."

As a Sunday School teacher, Miss Henrietta has spanned the years from 1897 to 1969. She is president of the Danville Woman's Missionary Union, a former president of Ebenezer WMU, and a former vice-president of East Central Division of the State WMU. For many years she served on the President's Council at Mercer University.

In one way Miss Agnes, an Episcopalian, admits giving in to Miss Henrietta, a Baptist. "Since I have no Episcopal church in Danville I have to go along with my deep-dyed Baptist sister," she says.

For twenty-five years Miss Agnes has been writing the local news for the *Twiggs County New Era,* the *Wilkinson County News,* and the *Macon Telegraph.* "Why," said Miss Henrietta, "at ten o'clock at night I hear her calling friends and asking them if they know any news. I tell her to stop all this business. She's been at it long enough." But Miss Agnes shakes her head. "I'm not going to quit. It keeps me young. Besides, these tidbits may make a best seller some day."

"We have enough memories and stories to tell, and I think we ought to write," Miss Henrietta admitted. "We want to write a book together, and Agnes wants to write a book about Dr. Crawford W. Long. Dr. Long was closely related to her mother, the former Leila Montgomery of Madison County. Agnes has been surrounded by doctors. Her father, I. Hamilton Goss of Athens, was a distinguished physician, and her brother, Ralph Goss of Athens, was a well-known surgeon. Agnes has had a long friendship with words. She is a graduate of Emory University, and for many years she was librarian at State Normal School in Athens."

It's a good thing Miss Henrietta wakes up before five o'clock in the morning. Otherwise the day at Magnolia Plantation would not be long enough. Their next exciting venture is to build a convalescent center. "We must remember the young as their years pile up," Miss Henrietta said with a smile.

Today, as in the days of the past, their home is noted for its hospitality. Neighbors, relatives. Rich, poor. Girls, boys. Farmers, statesmen. Miss Agnes recalls the special significance of Saturdays, for that was the day that Dudley Hughes went to town and invited every farmer in Twiggs County to go home with him for dinner. The only way that Mrs. Hughes could guess the number for dinner on Saturday was to peer through the curtain and see how many farmers were following Dudley Hughes through the woods. The members of FHA and FFA know that they too will find a welcome at Magnolia Plantation. Whether it is for tea, luncheon, or dinner, Miss Henrietta's blessing will warm the heart.

The two sisters have faith in the youth of today, but they believe that parents should spend more time at home with their children. "Children today do not have a chance," observed Miss Henrietta. "There are too many frustrations, too many pressures. We didn't have Little League, Big League and television, but we had plenty of fun. We went to square dances, ice cream festivals, candy pullings, tallyho parties, and we behaved ourselves. All my family rode horseback. My greatest happiness was riding over the plantation. Every girl and boy ought to have the pleasure that I had riding in a wagon pulled by two goats named Erwin and Dud. That was better than today's fastest car or biggest jet. What parents ought to realize is that a child can be happy at home as I have been."

Miss Henrietta regrets that she has given up horseback riding. "I ought to be on a horse right now," she said. But she has no intention of giving up her rifle practice. She has twelve-gauge and twenty-gauge shotguns. Also two pistols. If reptile lamentations could be heard, one rattlesnake would voice his regret on entering the backyard of Magnolia Plantation. One shot was all that Miss Henrietta needed.

The two sisters, young in spirit and enriched by wisdom, have much to be proud of in their heritage. Many honors and achievements pass in review: The launching of a ship, the S. S. Dudley M. Hughes, in Savannah in 1943; designation of Magnolia Plantation as a historical site by the John Ball Chapter of the DAR in 1955; dedication of the Dudley M. Hughes Vocational School in Macon; the Smith-Hughes School in Atlanta and scores of other schools that bear his name. At the State Archives is a pen that has helped millions of Americans—the pen used by President Wilson when he signed the Smith-Hughes Bill.

Perhaps the memorial that stands the tallest is the little chapel on a lake—a consummation of the spiritual influence of Mary and Dudley Hughes. Two sisters are remembering something that Dudley Hughes said fifty-three years ago:

"We are so busy with winning our way, so concerned with our own national, state, and local affairs that a great problem like the wasting of our youth has been almost untouched."

Tall trees stand guard over the little chapel built in their honor. A chapel made of granite cut out of the nearby hills. Since its dedication thousands of young people have entered the chapel for meditation and prayer. Sunlight coming through the stained-glass windows warms the bowed heads of the young. Few sounds break the silence of this cloistered place. Sometimes the organ is played and a bobwhite joins in with his call. Cicadas and bullfrogs do their own accompaniment. The lake makes no ripple of discontent.

On the lectern is an old Bible belonging to the Hughes family. The cathedral beams and the walnut pews are stained a silver gray. The carpet is red, and the altar chairs are covered with red velvet. On one side an encasement holds memorabilia of the Hughes family—historical papers, rare old pictures and books, and gavels made of magnolia wood and cedar from trees planted by Mr. and Mrs. Hughes on Magnolia Plantation.

At the entrance of the chapel is a bronze plaque:

Hughes Memorial Chapel

In Memory of

Dudley Mays Hughes
1847–1927

Co-Author National Vocational Education Act of 1917
and
Mary Dennard Hughes 1854–1954

Who shared his enduring faith in the youth of America
The soil of this country is the storehouse of all its wealth

Sitting beneath the shade of the trees at the chapel we watched the young folks stop and greet Miss Henrietta and Miss Agnes and thank them for their great gift.

"Use it, love it, take care of it," Miss Henrietta said.

1969

photo-sketch by Everett Saggus

The Nancy Hart cabin is located ten miles from Elberton near Wahatche Creek. Nancy Hart was famous for her bravery in holding off a party of British Tories until help arrived.

Revolutionary War Gun Found in Elbert County

Was It Pistol–totin' Nancy Hart's?

Dust off your Georgia history book, for red-headed Nancy Hart has again stepped out of its pages and assumed her beloved role of gun-totin', gun-shootin' Nancy!

Recently Tol Snellings, caretaker for the Nancy Hart cabin in Elbert County, went fox hunting, and about a mile from the cabin he came across a post oak tree that had died and had fallen. There nestled in its hollow trunk was an old muzzle-loader gun with a barrel thirty-nine inches long and with unused powder still in the muzzle. An authority on guns says that it is the type used during the Revolutionary period. The gun is in good condition despite the fact that squirrels and rabbits have chewed on it considerably.

According to Mr. Snellings, the Tories should have made an easy escape by the time Nancy got ready to shoot a gun of this type. "First you pour powder into the muzzle, pack paper on top of powder with a ramrod, then pour in shot," he explained. "Then pack paper on top of the shot, pull the hammer back, put cap on tube, and you are ready to shoot."

The caretaker, of course, cannot say that sharpshooting Nancy used the gun that he has found, but from the people who have thronged to see it and from the offers he has had for the gun, historical enthusiasts have drawn their own conclusions.

1949

Elbert County Churches: Looking Back at Their Beginnings

Although Elbert County had Methodist and Baptist churches before 1800, there was no church in Elberton until the organization of the First Methodist Church in 1815. A small white frame building with a bell in its steeple was erected on the site of the present Elbert County High School on College Avenue. In 1848 Dr. Henry Bourne, an Elberton physician, gave the church 2½ acres of land on the corner of Church and Thomas Streets. Here a larger building was erected almost on the site of the present Harris-Allen Library. It was a white frame building with a steeple. Soon a churchyard developed behind it.

The former building on College Avenue (then Elbert Street) became the village schoolhouse, taking the place of the ancient one-room building housing the local school. In 1848 the church trustees were Alfred Hammond, Amos Vail, W. A. Swift, Robert Hester, and another Mr. Vail. The church remained in the Elbert Circuit until 1880 and services were held twice a month on Saturdays and Sundays. The Elberton church was made a station in 1880 with J. H. Baxter, pastor.

The interior of the First Methodist Church of Elberton

In 1886 the present building of the First Methodist Church was erected. The Reverend J. W. Roberts, who was later president of Wesleyan College at Macon, was minister at the time. In 1908 the brick church was covered with stucco. The church will celebrate its one-hundred-fiftieth anniversary this year.

First Baptist Church

The First Baptist Church was organized in 1860. The little white frame church with a bell in its steeple was erected near the corner of Thomas and Elbert Streets. The charter members were: Mrs. George I. Barr, Mr. and Mrs. Thomas J. Heard, Mr. and Mrs. Joseph Y. Arnold, William H. Edwards, Dr. and Mrs. M. P. Deadwyler, Mr. and Mrs. L. W. Stevens, Mrs. Roebuck, Mr. Eaves, and perhaps others, but no further records are available. L. W. Stevens was the first minister. (In the church history the first minister's name is spelled Stevens but in McIntosh's *History of Elbert County* his name is spelled Stephens.)

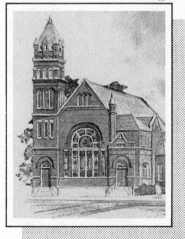

According to the church history the present building was made possible through the generosity of (Mrs. M. P.) Adeline Deadwyler who contributed one-half the cost. She also gave a large part of the furnishings and supplies. It is located on the corner of Heard and Thomas Streets. The cornerstone was laid on September 27, 1897. The First Baptist Church has made and approved plans for the building of a new sanctuary.

The First Baptist Church of Elberton

First Presbyterian Church

In 1865 the First Presbyterian Church was organized. The congregation met in the Methodist Church. Those joining the church at that time were: C. W. Fenton, John T. McCarty, Sophie G. Bruce, Rachel Auld, and Amos T. Akerman. Mr. Akerman was attorney general of the United States during Grant's administration. For more than twelve years the church had no building of its own. Meetings were held in the old Methodist Church.

Carolyn Cann

The First Presbyterian Church of Elberton

The Presbyterian Church was a little white frame building with bell and steeple located on McIntosh Street.

In 1904 the congregation began to plan a new church. Three trustees were elected in April 1905: W. M. Wilcox, Fred W. Auld, and E. P. Harris. After the death of Mr. Auld and Mr. Harris, W. N. Auld and W. L. Skelton became trustees. The present church stands upon the site of the old one. It was first occupied in 1909 and was dedicated in 1913.

In the early days, the First Methodist Church, the First Baptist Church, and the First Presbyterian Church were known as the Three Little White Churches Of The Bells. These churches are on the sites of three former circus rings in Elberton.

Everett Saggus

The Bethlehem Methodist Church

Bethlehem Methodist Church

Bethlehem Methodist Church in Elbert County is said to be the second oldest Methodist church in Georgia. According to Richard T. Lumpkin, minister of the Middleton Methodist Circuit, Bethlehem is the oldest active Methodist church and the oldest continuing congregation in Georgia Methodism. It was established in 1787 as Thompson's Meeting House and later changed its name to Bethlehem. Bishop Francis Asbury called the first Methodist Conference in Georgia in 1788 to meet at Thompson's Meeting House, but because of severe weather and the Bishop's illness the Conference actually was held in the home of Judge Charles Tait near Petersburg.

A new brick church has replaced the old Bethlehem Church. A communion table in the present church was made from some of the pews of the original church. A gavel from the wood of the old church was presented to Bishop John Owens Smith to be used to open Methodist Conferences.

Everett Saggus

The interior of historic Van's Creek Baptist Church in Ruckersville.

Van's Creek Baptist Church

Van's Creek Baptist Church in Ruckersville has a long and rich heritage. Although it is said to be the sixth Baptist church to be established in Georgia it is the oldest in continuous service. It was established in 1785 by the Reverend Dozier Thornton, Revolutionary soldier and Virginian. Van's Creek received its name from an Indian convert, David Vann, famous chief of the Cherokees.

In the Elberton Court House can be found the minutes of Van's Creek Church from 1785–1893. Some of the excerpts of the minutes in 1797 are:

One sister came forward with an acknowledgement for talking in anger and saying that which was not lawful. She was forgiven.

Brother Burk presented a query to the church: **Is it a Duty to support our Minister?** They voted affirmatively.

One sister was up in Conference for wearing a long plume on her hat. She asked forgiveness, removed the plume and all was well.

Even in 1797 the church felt a financial pinch as do the churches of today. Some of the year's contributions were: twenty-five cents, fifty cents, and seven cents.

Falling Creek Baptist Church and Others

Falling Creek Baptist Church was organized in 1788. The Reverend Thomas Maxwell was the leading force in establishing this church.

The Stinchcomb Methodist Church
in Elbert County

Other old churches in Elbert County include: Doves Creek, organized in 1788; Beaverdam Baptist Church, now Bethel Church, 1829; Antioch Baptist church, 1847; Rock Branch Baptist Church, 1845; Stinchcomb Methodist Church, 1794. Dionysius Oliver, Elbert County pioneer and the man who named Petersburg, is buried in the cemetery of this old church.

The Methodist Publishing House at Nashville, Tennessee, has presented a citation for continuous service to the Coldwater Methodist Church. The church is one hundred and seventy-five years old.

1965

Dinner for the Bishop

In going through old records of my church, Bethlehem Methodist Church in Elbert County, I read a story about James Osgood Andrew, born May 3, 1794. He was the son of John Andrew and Mary Cosby Andrew of Elbert County. John Andrew, an itinerant Methodist preacher, was the first native Georgian to be admitted to the Georgia Conference.

When James was a young boy, he joined the church during a camp meeting at Bethlehem Church. Since he was the only one who joined, the stewards didn't consider the meeting to be a success. They said, "Nobody joined but little Jimmie Andrew."

"Little Jimmie" followed in his father's footsteps and became a preacher. When he preached for the first time at Bethlehem, the only invitation he received for dinner was from a Negro woman. Their meal consisted of corn bread and sweet potatoes.

Years later, after becoming well known as a bishop, he preached again at Bethlehem, and many members invited him for dinner. But the one invitation he accepted was from the same faithful Negro woman who had befriended him so many years before. —Inez Balchin Langston

The First Day at Young Harris

by John G. Logan

I was born and reared in Brasstown Valley, one and one-half miles below the present site of Young Harris College. From my earliest recollection I had a thirst for knowledge. Possibly the most highly prized moment ever to touch my life was the founding of the above-named institution.

Well do I remember that momentous Monday morning in January 1886, when I set out to realize my life's ideal. I rejoice today, more than ever, that on this first Monday morning I lent my influence and presence in starting off dear old Young Harris. The sun was shining beautifully that morning. The road was frozen several inches deep, and when thoroughly thawed was almost impassable. I made this one-and-one-half-mile journey on foot.

The "automobile" of those days was an ordinary horse and buggy or an old-time ox wagon. It was nothing unusual for the front axle to scrape the road. Walking was preferable.

Old Cedar and Double Knobs were in their glory that morning. Draped in their polar ermine, they seemed to smile upon a lonely lad on his way to gratify the highest ambition of his young heart.

Our small clan soon gathered. I say *clan* advisedly. For Young Harris students are noted, the world over, for their brotherly love for each other. The very day this institution of learning was born, this spirit of love also came into being. God grant that it may never die!

Enrolled the first morning were Ida Stephens, John G. Logan, Will T. Hunt, Elijah Morgan, Sallie Erwin, Will Daniel, and Candace Matheson.

The old-fashioned wood fire, glowing from the old-time fireplace, gave us a royal welcome that frosty morning. The storehouse, about which we have heard so much through the fifty years gone by, where Young Harris was started, had two small rooms, with a porch on the front, jutting close upon the big road. Our educational equipment consisted of a few rickety chairs and two or three uncomfortable benches.

Reverend Mark Edwards, of the North Georgia Conference, was the first teacher. Brother Edwards had two jobs: he had been sent by his conference to organize a school somewhere in the Brasstown Valley and to serve as pastor of the Towns Mission. If any man ever did the work of the pioneer it was Reverend Mark H. Edwards.

How ardently he prayed that first morning that God would watch over the school and bless its service to the rising generations. The thousands of pupils today, scattered over our vast domain, are the answer to his prayers.

Author's Note: Mr. Logan served as pastor of the First Methodist Church in Elberton, where he resided after his retirement from the ministry.

Looking Back at the News

Recently in replacing old monuments with new, several Harmony Blue granite workers of Elberton turned back the pages of history thirty-one years when they found an October 26, 1910, copy of the *Atlanta Journal* in a cement monument erected over the grave of John Stonecypher, near Avalon in Stephens County.

On that particular day in history, William Howard Taft was president; it was predicted that scientific methods would quadruple the cotton crop; twenty-cent cotton seemed probable; Honorable George M. Napier, of Macon, headed Georgia Masons; there was a need for only one naval station in the South, according to Secretary of Navy Meyer; the death of Allen D. Candler, former Georgia governor was reported; Alan R. Hawley and Augustus Post were the world's balloon champions after traveling from St. Louis, Missouri, to Quebec at an average rate of thirty-five miles an hour; a little bullpup defied Atlanta women, and police were called; Wagner's opera *Tannhauser* was to be rendered on the auditorium organ for ten cents; there was a contest giving away a seventy-dollar buggy and a twenty-dollar harness; an advertisement urged would-be musicians to learn to play the piano or organ in one hour; live geese feathers were for sale; editorials promoted Clean-up Day; and there was a humorous article on "Why Whiskers?"

They also discovered that the younger generation was even then going to the dogs. A very upset young man wrote in "Our Household" column: "I am distressed at the immodesty, lightheadedness and frivolity of the girls of today." And a letter from a woman admitted, "The hand that rocks the cradle rules the world. It may be she could rule better with one hand on the cradle and in the other equal rights."

They found that even in 1910 lonely and disillusioned men were seeking lovelorn advice. Quote: "Lonely cowboy, remember there are plenty of good true girls. Your heart is sore now, but you will see the day that you can say to some nice girl that you love her more than you ever loved that coquette; your affection for a true girl will be deeper because of the sad experience you are undergoing."

Oh, for the good old days!

1941

Proud Old Homes Of Elbert County

Though Elbert County suffered one of its greatest historical losses in 1964 when Rose Hill was destroyed by fire, there are still many beautiful homes of the antebellum period left standing. Proudly they bespeak a gracious way of life.

Memories of Rose Hill will linger long in the minds of those who enjoyed the hospitality for which it was famous.

Built in 1828 by Stephen Heard's widow, Elizabeth Darden Heard, for their youngest son, Thomas Jefferson Heard and his bride, Nancy Middleton, the hall and dining room panelling as well as the main stairway of the former Stephen Heard home in Heardmont were installed at Rose Hill.

The beautiful stairway was used in the filming of the great epic motion picture *Birth of a Nation*.

In the 1890s two wings, Essex and Wessex were added to the original home by Mr. and Mrs. Eugene B. Heard, who lived there for many years. It was there in 1892 that Mrs. Heard organized the Sorosis Club, which became Georgia's oldest Federated Woman's Club.

Rose Hill Plantation was built in 1828 by Stephen Heard's widow, Elizabeth Darden Heard for their youngest son, Thomas Jefferson Heard, and his bride, Nancy Middleton.

Descendants of the Ralph Banks family still make pilgrimages to this historic home now known as Coldwater Plantation and owned by descendants of James and Ida Jones Hammond, who bought it about fifty years ago. The first annual conference of the Methodist Church is said by some historians to have met here many years ago.

Built "before the War" as a wedding gift to Asa and Lauriette Hamilton Chandler, this home on Old Petersburg Road has been the residence of the Walter C. Jones family for more than fifty years. It is listed on the National Register of Historic Places.

The Moses Fleming Adams home on McIntosh Street is more than a century old. It has been occupied by four generations of the Adams family.

Everett Saggus

When William Harper built his home on College Avenue in 1854, he wanted to protect his daughters from the eyes of guests as the daughters went up and down the stairs of the house in their hoop skirts, so he insisted that the stairway be built in the back of the house.

Everett Saggus

Miss Eleanor Oliver, a descendant of Dionysius Oliver, lives in this home on McIntosh Street. The home was built in the 1850s by James C. Harper and William A. Swift with granite quarried and set by Daniel Olds.

Everett Saggus

It was also at Rose Hill that Mrs. Heard established the famous Seaboard Air Line Traveling Library in memory of a son who died at the age of twelve. With the cooperation of railroad officials, this library, which grew to include 50,000 volumes, sent books into any area served by the Seaboard Air Line that would request them. There were no dues, no fines, no fees.

On these pages are pictured six of the oldest and most interesting houses in Elberton and Elbert County. They are only a sample of the many beautiful homes in the "Granite City"—homes that are interesting both architecturally and historically.

1965

Excerpts from the 1863–1864 Diary of John Henry Fortson

John Henry Fortson was a Baptist minister, teacher, Confederate soldier, and chaplain in the War Between the States. He was born in Elbert County, Georgia, September 20, 1837. He died March 27, 1908. He was converted and joined the church of Falling Creek, Elbert County, and was baptized by the Reverend Asa Chandler. He preached in Wilkes County, Columbia County, Lincoln County, and Elbert County. On March 31, 1864, he married Julia Isabelle Anderson of Wilkes County. She was born March 8, 1847, and died June 18, 1929. The Reverend Mr. Fortson and Mrs. Fortson had thirteen children, and all thirteen children were baptized by their father.

Mr. Fortson's great-granddaughter, Josephine Fortson Oglesby (Mrs. George T. Oglesby) of Elberton has a pocket diary that he kept in 1863 and 1864. The following excerpts from the diary range from the courtship of John Henry Fortson and Julia Isabelle Anderson to the war-torn South.

Sept. 16

At two o'clock A.M. I left for the train, arrived there at nine. Took the train at half past nine for Atlanta. Met many Soldiers of my acquaintance. Met more at Union Point, arrived at Atlanta about dark. Stopped all night with D. A. & Eliz. Fortson under the carshed.

Sept. 17

Took the cars again at eight o'clock. We passed on to Tunnel Hill. Many of us walked. We passed by the Rail Road bridges burned. We passed by Ring Gold about 5 miles. We met some wounded men.

Sept. 18

We went to Hood's division Hospital. I found many of my friends wounded. William E. Fortson and I then left for the cars. At nine the battle opened furiously. I heard the battle all day. Many came in and others were brought in the Hospital. *Badly* wounded. This was an awful day with me. I saw many legs & arms amputated. Some men were shot almost in pieces.

Sept. 19

The wounded still come in until late in the night. Gen. Hood is brought in. His leg is amputated high up. He said, "As long as I have a leg or an arm, and I can ride a horse, and command such men as I do, I will fight those Yankees." I waited upon the wounded all day. They need much help.

Sept. 20

The wounded are yet brought in. Gen. Hood taken off on litter by twenty-four men to Col. Little's. I walk over the Battle field. See many signs of death, many dead men. See Bro. Edd Dickenson. Stay with him all night.

Sept. 21

Returned to the Hospital. Wait upon the wounded all day. E. B. Taite is brought to the Hospital. He was badly wounded. I helped to bring him into a stall. I wait upon him Especially. Many die. Many call for help during the night but cannot get their nurses to come. I almost wear myself out for want of sleep & rest. Some rain.

Went to Elberton. Bro. Asa Chandler went with me. Gave in Confederate tax.

Sept. 22

Capt. Willis, Capt. Burch, Capt. Callaway and many others leave for Atlanta. About thirty wagons were loaded with the wounded and sent to the Depot. I am much fatigued, for want of Sleep and rest. The dust can barely be stood. Day cloudy and damp. Went to the wool factory & carried Mrs. Heard and Mrs. Sutton wool.

Sept. 23

About thirty wagons loaded with the wounded are sent to Tunnel Hill. Mr. Peak comes to see his son. His son has the lockjaw. I pray with and for his son. Uncle E. B. Taite & L. W. Stephens come to see us. We are glad to see them.

Sept. 24

L. W. Stephens and Uncle E. B. Taite went over the battle field. Stephens and I went to see the 18th Reg. near Chattanooga. The Boys are in fine Spirits. I spent the night with them.

Sept. 25

The Brigade is ordered off to throw up breast works. Stephens and I go up upon the Lookout Mountain. We go upon the Point of Rocks. We see all the Yankees work strength. At night Stephens preached to the 18th Reg. "Lord, help me." I close by exhortation. The meeting is well attended.

Oct. 2

Day pleasant. I am quite sick with chill and fever today. Rev. Harber preached today and tonight. The Reg. goes to the line of breast works. Two cannons are fired. Anderson's train moves.

Oct. 3

I am much better. I walk with the Reg. I go upon the Lookout Mountain. The bombardment of Chattanooga begins. No great damage is done to the enemy. The bombardment opened at 10½ and closed at 5 o'clock P.M.

Oct. 5

Go up to the Reg. get letter & money to take home for the Soldiers friends. Tell them goodbye. Start with Jno. Pullen to Atlanta. Took the train at 7 o'clock P.M. Went to Tunnel Hill. Spent the night in a house with some Soldiers. We had nothing to eat but two loaves of bread and some syrup.

Oct. 6, 1863

Took the train at 7 o'clock A.M. We get breakfast at Tunnel Hill. Bought some pies to eat. Went direct to Atlanta. I took John Pullen to the distribution Hospital. I took supper at the Atlanta Hotel. I slept in Hospital with John Pullen. Waited on the sick by distributing cover and helping two others.

Oct. 7, 1863

Saw the sick leave toward Montgomery. Saw Samuel Burney and Judge Morrow. Went to Tombs' Regiment. Saw and talked with many acquaintances.

Oct. 8

Went with Brown to Atlanta, saw Nat Hunter at the train. Saw Col. Willis at Greensboro. Saw John Hawkins at Union Point.

Oct. 12

High fever. I take some tea, bathe my feet.

Oct. 13

Fever yet. I take a toddy. Take some teas. I am no better. Took the cars at Washington at 10 o'clock. Arrived in Augusta at 5. Took tea with Mr. S. W. Heard. Formed the acquaintance of Miss Julia Burney of Madison, Ga. Slept at the Globe Hotel. Paid ten dollars.

Oct. 14

I feel a little better. This morning my fever is off. I take quinine. I take 10 drops of Sandamun, teaspoonful of sweet oil. Dr. Albert Mathews comes to see me. He thinks I am doing very well. He leaves quinine & opium pills for me to take.

Nov. 9

Spent the day at Goshen. Read the Testament and the History of Providence. Went to Bro. A. Oglesby's. And to Mr. Crook's to get a slay.

Dec. 2

At Uncle E. K. Fortson. Several Ladies and Gentlemen came in the evening. Mr. and Mrs. Bishop, Miss Neely from Griffin, Miss Nelms, Miss

Jane Witcher, Dr. May, Mr. Dillard, Mr. Whittington, Texas Soldier. We pulled candy at night. Had a fine time.

Dec. 6

Went to Griffin, Athens, Atlanta, Union Point. Miss Cornelia Edwards, Miss Durham and Cousin Hortense Kinnebrew came down to meet me. I saw many of my friends at Union Point. Some going to the War. The Ladies and I went to Stephens Depot and spent the night at J. Kennebrew. Bro. Asa met me.

Dec. 25

This morning I marry my first black couple of Cousin B. W. Fortson. I went to Church. No preaching.

Dec. 29

Today we bid farewell to the year 1863. May I do more good the next and may God pardon the errors of this and give me grace for the year 1864. Amen.

January 1, 1864

This is the first day of 1864. In the morning at Mr. Fleming Adams in Elberton. Dined at Uncle Dozier Thornton. Spent the night at W. S. Campbell's.

May I spend this year in the service of God. May I labor with the zeal of an apostle. May the Lord bless my churches, bless me and do much good through me as his instrument. May I seek the interest of God and his people above everything else. Amen.

The weather is very cold, windy and disagreeable.

March 2

Weather moderate. I did not teach school that I might go to Beulah and hear Rev. Selvage preach. He did not come. I sent a note to Miss Belle Anderson. I feel a little unwell.

March 4

Weather pleasant cloudy. Went to Bro. Marshel. Spent the night. Met Miss Belle Anderson. Had a pleasant time.

March 5

Rained in morning. The day was pleasant. Went to Church at Rehoboth. Miss Belle in the buggy with me. I tried to preach from Psalms 15: 12, 13. Heard two colored men relate their christian experience & they were received into the Church. Bro. Hogan & I went to Sister Cornelison's & spent the night. Miss Belle stayed with Sister Muligan tonight.

March 6

Went to Church at Rehoboth. Heard the children recite their Sabbath School lesson. I baptized two Servants Alexander & Henry. This was my first effort. Heard Bro. Wright preach from Rom. 1:16. "For I am not ashamed of the Gospel of Christ." I dined with Sister Arnet. Miss Belle & I went home. We partially engaged that we would marry. Miss Belle is to answer the 8th.

March 7

Weather pleasant. Received a note from Miss Belle. She gave her full consent to be my spouse. She said her mother is willing also.

March 12

Weather pleasant. Went to Church at Goshen. Tried to preach from Psalms 17:55. "The salvation of the righteous is of the Lord." Spent the night with Bro. Sale. Bro. Hogan also with me. Received a note from Miss Belle saying that she proposed to wait until she saw me before she said when we would marry.

March 13

Weather very cold. Go to Mrs. Anderson's. Miss Belle and I agree to marry on Thursday night the 31 of this month.

March 31

Weather pleasant though we have frost every morning. Went to Mrs. Anderson's. Miss Julia Anderson and I were joined in holy wedlock at nine (9) o'clock. The ceremony was performed by the Rev. Thomas Wright. Miss Fannie Heard & Mrs. ———— Marshel stood up with us. Quite a number of persons were present. I have felt unwell all day.

April 1

During last night it began to rain. The morning was quite unlikely with rain & mist. It changed for better about 9 o'clock. Belle and I started for Elbert at 8 ¾ o'clock. We go to Pa's at 3 o'clock. We found Pa quite sick of Pneumonia. It hardly appears that he can recover. I went to bed sick. I had fever all day.

April 3

Day pleasant. I am much better, up today. Pa is about the same. Grand Ma was attacked with Pneumonia severely. Dr. Mathews gave us a tincture of iron composed of about one teaspoonful of copper, two of alum, a few grains of salt put in 1½ pints of water.

April 8

Grand Ma was buried at 3 o'clock P.M. Aunt Lucy A. and Hooter Kinnebrew & Aunt Lou Mills came at dark. They were too late to see Grand Ma. Pa is no better that I can see.

April 11

Day pleasant. Pa is quite unwell. The inflammation reaches around him. We put cream & Elm poltice on him. We sent for Dr. Deadwyler. He told us that erysipelas had taken place on Pa. He put Iodine around the erysipelas, but it had gone too far. Gangrene takes place in the blister on his side. His pulse declines.

April 12

Pa is so ill he died at eleven o'clock in the morning.

April 13

Father was put in the coffin about one o'clock. Bro. Asa Chandler came and preached at three from Rev. 21:4. "And God shall wipe away all tears from their eyes; and there shall be no more death, neither sorrow, nor crying, neither shall there be any more pain; for the former things are passed away." Many persons were present. We buried him at 4:14. Uncle Dozier Thornton spent the night with us. My throat was sore.

April 19

Dined with Uncle Dozier Thornton. Went to Elberton. Robert Heard and Miss Lou Jones married tonight.

April 17

Went to the Episcopal Church in the morning to the Dutch Reform in the afternoon and to the Catholic in the evening.

May 5

Weather warm & dry. Had the sheep brought up & sheared. My wife and I went to Danburg, spent the night at John Anderson's.

July 23

Heard bad news from Atlanta, viz. that it was taken, our army demoralized that the road to Madison was torn up, that Athens was almost taken or would be in a few minutes . . . Received of Mr. Williams' wife & Drury Cade 26 dollars for preaching.

July 24

Went to Church at Friendship tried to preach from Eph. 6:11. "Put on the whole armor of God that ye may be able to stand against the wiles of the devil." Heard much better news that Atlanta was not taken, the army was in good spirits, and that we had quite a success. Athens was not taken.

Christmas, New Year's, & a Spring Spree

Quit looking at the taillight of the old year and turn on the headlight of the new year.

—*The Reverend Roscoe Simpson*

Georgia's First Christmas Tree

Carolyn Cann

This cottage on Heard Street in Elberton was the home of George and Henrietta Loehr, who brought the tradition of the Christmas tree from their native Germany to Georgia. The house is still known as the Christmas Tree House and is the home of the Elbert County Historical Society.

When the season of Christmas draws near and the ice begins to cling close to the pines and cedars, it brings recollections of the George Loehr family going into the deep woods in Elberton to select their evergreen tree. It was a time of joy and excitement, with the children scampering, trying to match their father's footsteps, and the oldest child carrying the axe. It is believed that Henrietta and George Loehr, who left Germany to come to America, were the first to decorate a Christmas tree in Georgia in the late 1850s in an attractive cottage on Heard Street in Elberton.

After Henrietta Leopole and George Loehr were married in their native Germany, they brought with them to America their most treasured possessions, a handsomely carved walnut bedroom suite and a cedar chest that showed the skilled craftsmanship of George Loehr as a cabinet maker. Within the cedar chest were Henrietta Loehr's silk shawl from China, her fine linens spun from flax, and her feather bed.

The Loehrs lived in New York for some time, but a big city did not appeal to the young couple, so they moved to Elberton, a little town in northeast Georgia. They built a cottage on Heard Street, which according to the Elbert County courthouse records was on "the road leading from the courthouse to Petersburg." The cottage is now known as the Christmas Tree House, and it is the home of the Elbert County Historical Society, which was founded in 1975.

According to an article written by Herbert Wilcox in the *Atlanta Journal and Constitution Magazine* in 1958, the young couple "not only brought their treasured possessions and useful skills to America. They also brought fond memories of their childhood in the fatherland. One of the most vivid was that of the Christmas trees that had delighted the children of Germany even before the United States became a nation—a lovely custom which the German people are credited with having given to the world."

The Loehrs had six children, three girls and three boys. The parents took great delight in giving them a Christmas just as they had known and loved in their native land.

Mrs. S. A. Gaines of Marietta, the last surviving granddaughter of the Loehrs, recalls the stories her parents and relatives told of how they decorated the first Christmas tree in Georgia. Each member of the family made decorations, and the tree was filled with multicolored paper chains, streamers, popcorn, apples, cookies, wooden toys, and animals. Little wooden candleholders held the candles that symbolized the light of the world.

George Loehr not only made intricately carved ornaments out of wood, but he also built a miniature picket fence that encircled the Christmas tree.

After the holiday season was over, the objets d'art and certain gifts were packed away to await the coming of another Christmas. It was an old German custom that some of the same gifts would reappear under the tree year after year.

The grandchildren of the Loehrs never grew tired of the stories their parents told them about the Christmases of long ago. They were fascinated by the German custom of the Christmas tree, which began in the eighth century when St. Boniface dedicated a fir tree to the Holy Child. A medieval custom depicted the Garden of Eden with a fir tree decorated with apples. This custom associated the birth of Christ with the evergreen. The first Christmas trees in Germany were decorated with apples, the symbols of Adam's fall, and round wafers representing the Sacred Host, which signified redemption. Later the apples and wafers were replaced by Christmas cookies.

The most popular legend, however, tells that the first Christmas tree was cut down by Martin Luther, who brought it home and decorated it with candles to imitate the "starry skies of Bethlehem that Holy Night."

Evergreens, symbolic of life after death, were used throughout the home. A swag above the doorway signified "This is a house where Christ abides." A wreath of holly represented Christ's crown of thorns, and the red berries, His drops of blood.

No descendant of the Loehr family knows what happened to the Christmas tree ornaments or the cedar chest in which they were stored. But fortunately members of the Howell Bagwell family have the walnut bed, dresser, and washstand that his great-great grandfather made and brought from his native land. They also have some of the fine old linens and the Chinese shawl brought from Germany. Howell Bagwell of Marietta is the son of Mrs. S. A. Gaines.

The first Christmas tree in America is said to have been decorated in the German immigrant community of Lancaster, Pennsylvania, in 1821, and the first national recognition of the Christmas tree came in 1856 when Nathaniel Hawthorne's old friend Franklin Pierce decorated one at the White House. So Henrietta and George Loehr bestowed upon Elberton and Georgia a legacy of Christmas magic, Georgia's first Christmas tree.

Each December in this cottage filled with reminders of a great heritage is a beautiful Christmas tree decorated in memory of Henrietta and George Loehr and their six children, and for everyone whose heart is filled with the joy of Christmas.

1982

Frank Downs Remembers

Members of a Methodist church at Bogart got together every year at Christmas time. They drew names and exchanged gifts. John Luke Adams never opened his gift. "No use," he said. "I reckon I'll get the same thing I always get from the dime store."

Finally he was persuaded to open his package. When he did he said, "See, I told you so."

The Reverend Harper Heard's Holiday Reminiscences

Let's get through picking cotton by Thanksgiving. We caught all the possums we could before Thanksgiving. A dozen possums or more. Mother fixed possum, sweet potatoes, buttermilk, cornbread and biscuits. My biggest hobby was rabbit, possum, and bird hunting. I still hunt. My eyesight is good in my nineties.

We'd have a keg or barrel of persimmon beer. We would let locusts and persimmons stand until they worked. We had a keg for Thanksgiving, Christmas, and one for New Year's Eve. Persimmon beer has a little kick. We took a wooden barrel, knocked head out of barrel and sawed the head. We topped it back up, not tight. We had holes at bottom and a wooden peg at bottom. Beer would come out at the bottom.

On Christmas Eve we'd go to bed and start peeking around for Santa Claus. Sure we believed in him. I went barefooted until Christmas. Didn't want to get shoes messed up for Christmas. Gifts: China doll, sleeping doll, wagon, candy, apples, oranges, bananas.

On New Year's Day we ate peas, hog jowl, milk, cornbread. Father's blessing: Good Lord, make us truthful and thankful for the nourishment of our bodies. Amen.

Christmas dinner: Possum at one end of the table and a boiled hen at the other. No matter how you cook chicken, no way is it as good as a tenderly boiled hen. Biscuits, corn bread. Take your pick. Chocolate cake, plain pound cake.

Mother's blessing: Lord, bless this meal to Thy good and to Thy glory.

The Christmas Bundle, a Short Story

Along toward the middle of December, the ice started clinging close to the cedars and pines, and the grass in the field glittered in the sun. The stiff shoulders of wintertime advised folks in North Georgia to store up kindling and logs aplenty for the wintry blasts to come.

In the 1800s John Beacon and his grandson Benjamin made morning trips into the woods to find kindling. Some folks called it *lighterd*. Whatever the name, it warmed the hearts and the hearths of many families in the country. When six-year-old Benjamin found his first kindling he squared his little shoulders.

"That's good, my boy," said Grandpa, "you'll help to keep us warm. You are just what Amanda and I have been needing."

In the days that followed, Benjamin felt a new freedom as he entered the forest alone. He looked a wildcat straight in the eye and took a step forward just like his grandpa had done. The wildcat took a step backward and disappeared. The rabbits and squirrels did not run away from him like they used to. The forest was a magic place. An old sycamore tree provided shade for him to sit and rest awhile.

He longed to hear the sound of his mother's voice and his father's laughter. Why did they leave him? Grandma Amanda said it was a typhoid fever epidemic. Whatever an epidemic was, it meant one thing to little Benjamin. His mama and papa did not answer when he called.

When Benjamin heard the old cow horn, he knew it was time to help milk the cows and get ready for supper. After the work was finished, he liked to sit on the back porch steps with his grandpa.

"Tomorrow we're going hunting," John Beacon announced. "I've taught you how to load and shoot a gun, and if you aim in the right direction, we'll have plenty of meat for Christmas. Your eyes are brighter than mine, and you'll bring down the game with my gun."

Early the next morning Benjamin wrapped his little coat tight around him and followed his grandpa into the icy woods. Suddenly he heard a leaf crackle. A wild pig grunted in friendly greeting. A cottontail rabbit circled around the young hunter and did a fearless cottontail dance. In a hickory tree a fat squirrel wriggled his bushy tail and plopped a hickory nut on top of Benjamin's head. As the squirrel raced down the tree, he swished and swirled his tail in merry greeting. One by one, as if on parade, he saw a wild turkey, a goose, and a quail.

His hands trembled as he took his grandpa's gun and aimed at a turkey. It was no use. How could he shoot the ones who had befriended him and taught him the way of the woods?

"I just can't, Grandpa," Benjamin sobbed.

Grandpa encircled Benjamin in his arms and said softly, "It's all right."

As they entered the back yard, two fat hens and four little pigs and their mama welcomed them home.

"Well, Benjamin, it looks like we'll have to get our meat from our own back yard," Grandpa observed.

"But they're our friends," the young child objected. "They follow you and Grandma and me every day."

John Beacon smiled. "You're right, my boy. There's no reason to sacrifice our friends. What could be better at Christmas than beans and corn pudding and your grandma's blueberry pie?"

The young boy nudged up close. "Nothing, Grandpa."

Benjamin felt like shouting with joy. What was there to fear when you had a grandpa by your side and a grandma in the kitchen?

At suppertime John Beacon bowed his head and asked the blessing. "Dear Father, we thank Thee for this beautiful day that has passed. We thank Thee for our daily bread and for our many blessings. Bless all people everywhere. Above all, we thank Thee for Thy guidance and we pray Thee to be with us and lead us and guide us always. Amen."

After supper Amanda walked up the steep steps to the cabin loft and tucked her grandson in his bed. Late that night Amanda and John sat and watched the logs burn low and turn to glowing embers.

"What's that sound, Amanda?"

"Somebody's stirring."

"Benjamin?"

"Yes, Grandpa."

"It's Christmas Eve. Get in that bed and go to sleep."

"I'm not sleepy, Grandpa."

"Grandpa walked to the bottom of the stairway. "What's bothering you, son?"

"I want a good day tomorrow."

"Christmas gifts and dinner?"

"No, Grandpa, I just want us to be together."

"What else, Benjamin?"

"*Lighterd.*"

"We have enough."

"But what about Mary and her baby? Don't you know that barn is cold?"

Grandpa rubbed his chin. "Well, no, not as long as lambs have wool soft enough to cradle a corner in the stable."

"Can a little pig help Mary and her baby and my mama and papa?"

It took awhile for Grandpa to reclaim his voice.

"Benjamin, when you have lived as long as I have, you will know that there is no animal as smart as the pig. He will be a watchman for Mary and the Christ Child. And for your mama and papa."

"What about the robin?"

Grandpa put his strong arms around the little child and said, "The robin is the winged gift of Christmas. He found out a long time ago that his brown breast became blood red because of the cruelty of man."

"I don't understand, Grandpa."

"Someday you will. The robin can weather all seasons. He knows the ways of the wind and the snow. Joy and grief. But most of all, he knows the needs of Mary and her son."

Outside in the clean, cold snow, there were flurries tapping on the windowpane. Inside, the flames in the fireplace made wispy shadows on the wall. A kitten purred, moved close to the warmth of the hearth, and curled into a circle. On the other side of the fireplace lay John Beacon's old hound dog dreaming the dreams of a faithful friend.

In the quiet folds of the little cabin, Amanda, John, and Benjamin listened to the crowing of the chanticleer. The morning herald of Christmas.

Benjamin ran up the steps to his room in the loft and raced down with three gifts.

For Amanda there was a gold locket—his mother's locket. For John there was a watch that belonged to Benjamin's father. The third gift was clutched close in his small hands. The time was right for Benjamin to set his mind at rest. "Grandma and Grandpa, does the baby Jesus have someone to love Him like you love me?"

Grandma drew nearer to her grandchild. "Yes, Benjamin, just like you."

In the child's hands was a bundle of kindling tied with a big red bow. "Is this enough to keep the baby Jesus warm?"

"Yes, Benjamin, it is enough to warm the whole wide world."

An Old New Year's Eve Custom

In the hill country of Georgia, there is an old New Year's Eve custom where a family bids farewell to the old year and waits with solemn stillness for the new one. The family gathers around in a circle as the shadows of evening fall. A log fire slowly burns and memories of the old year seem to blend into the flickering flames and hot red ashes on the hearth.

The father goes into the kitchen and returns with a large white bowl filled with water from the old well. He is the first to wash his hands. Then the mother washes her hands and the hands of the baby cradled in her arms. One by one the children go through the cleansing ritual.

With head bowed the father says a simple prayer: "Most holy One, thank You for this bowl. It is not big enough to wash away all the mistakes that we have made in the past, but please give us the grace and strength to begin again with clean hands."

Spring Shopping Spree

In the spring a young man's fancy may turn lightly to love and fond affection, but Georgia women, be they old or young, claimed or unclaimed, dream of stunning suits and shocking hats and subsequently, a spring spree to Atlanta.

No humming of locusts overhead can equal the buzzing preparations of small-town women as they lay plans for a spring shopping day in Atlanta. Business girls boldly ask their bosses for a day off (with pay), preferably on Saturday, so they can get in the real rush of things. Struggling housewives who are tired of their squawling bundles from Diaperville and equally fed up with their till-the-end-of-time bargains, miraculously find a mother-in-law or a sitter who is willing to run all day after the children, and quietly announce that they have a lift to Atlanta. They solemnly promise to bring Johnny a Sunday suit and little Susie an Easter frock. And, of course, they might just look around for something on the bargain racks to cover their own threadbare backs.

On another side of the fence are the tired and worn-out schoolmarms who hope to goodness that a new suit and a sassy hat will not be wasted merely on the superintendent and the board of trustees.

And in small towns all over Georgia are the highly successful campaigners, the blushing brides-to-be, who think that Atlanta and a trousseau are synonymous and who, with all the others, turn their cars toward the capital city in search of everything from chaste white nightgowns to devilishly alluring black ones. Besides cars uncountable, women board crowded busses and equally crowded trains, just on account of spring and sap rising and such stuff.

Upon arrival in Atlanta, a light breakfast is in order. After a serving of orange juice, two eggs, a slab of ham, toast and coffee, the referee at last says "go," and the small-town darlings begin their scrambling. Some scramble for shoes first, for they have learned from experience that if they are buying their shoes to inveigle approval from the opposite sex they had better buy them soon after reaching the city. If, however, they are buying them to suit their corns and calluses, it's pretty smart to wait around till afternoon, for feet that have pounded those gate city pavements all day long are not only tired and sore but probably a couple of sizes bigger than when they started.

In another department a sweet young thing from the red old hills has

If blondes, widowers, or redheads are the first to cross the threshold on New Year's Day, they may create problems.

—old-time Georgia superstition

whipped out her CHARGAPLATE (this undoubtedly deserves caps) after finding a suit that the saleswoman declares is the only one of its kind in captivity. And, after trying on scads of spring prints, the shrewd buyer decides on a $24.98 number in morose black which she simply knows is a bargain because Jenny Westbrook bought the very same model in red not more than three months ago, and she certainly paid $49.95 for it. And now, little lady, go on over to the hat department and get that gorgeous Milly Sachay and cut corners some other way.

Aching bones and gnawing pains in the middle suggest to the small-town slickers that it's time to grab a sandwich. "But surely you want more than a measly old sandwich," laments one. "Well, yes," it's agreed, "shopping is better on a full stomach." So again it's the works, everything from soup to nuts.

Sundry, mundane, and slightly surprising are the reasons for so many out-of-town women going to Atlanta. For instance, one girl goes on an average of every two weeks to exchange a foundation garment (corset to you) for her mother. Another Georgia heartbreaker, slightly giddy, was told what she needed to lure men was Chanel No. 5, so she beat it to Atlanta and asked for something in Chenille. She was a shade befuddled when the saleslady planked out a bedspread.

Another maiden's favorite stopping place in Atlanta is a certain jewelry store. She likes the management so well that she even asks them if they might help her to needlepoint or just where is the best place to have her alligator heels built up. Then there is the girl who shops only for her family. She heads straight for the gentlemen's sturdy-longhandle department and asks for some shorts. "What size does your husband wear, madam?" "I don't have one," she beefs, "but I have got a daddy, and he bulges around the middle."

A few flighty purchases before the stores close. The almost forgotten comics for the almost forgotten husbands and babes, and finally, a last stop at a market for salt-rising bread and cake and then, homeward bound. For many miles the lights stay on in cars until the last lovely package is sufficiently oohed and ahed over. Busses leaving Atlanta, trains pulling out. Goodbye, Peachtree.

Two days later. Scene 1. Post offices all over Georgia.

Characters: Every woman who went to Atlanta busy returning some of the stuff that didn't fit or that she couldn't afford.

1947

The Lighter Side of Life

Live slow, eat light, worry light, and laugh full.

—*Berry Watkins*

Ladies and Gentlemen . . .

A speaker has virtually no problems. On being invited to give a ten-minute talk he is apt to unravel a thirty- to forty-minute oration of stentorian splendor. Following a full, bosomy front of an introduction he assumes a cloak of modesty for praise well-deserved. But it appears he expected even more.

He reaches into the shredded pocket where jokes lie huddled and weary, and he tells his favorite yarn. There is a pause for fully expected clapping and laughter. He proceeds to follow his outline, deviating only for pet stories, theories, peeves, and hobbies.

Fearing possible dehydration, he refreshes himself with water. There is an appropriate pause for the long, inspirational gulp.

Customarily a speaker stays with the audience long after chairs begin to creak, fidgeting humans tip loudly up the stairs, and bright eyes grow glazed and dim.

And so it is. A speaker has virtually no problems. But—the listeners do!

A Man of Few Words

A mountaineer sauntered into one of the largest jewelry stores in Atlanta. A saleswoman gave him a cordial smile and asked if she could be of help, but he made no reply. He went over to a showcase filled with diamonds. In a few minutes he motioned to the saleswoman for assistance and pointed to one particularly beautiful gem.

"Wrop it," he said.

The saleswoman followed directions. When she presented him with the little beribboned package she said, "That will be fifteen hundred dollars, tax included."

The mountaineer levelled a long look at her. Shifting his eyes to his recent purchase he said, "Unwrop it."

The Manicure Set

Years ago patients didn't get out of breath running to pay their doctors' bills. Dr. D. N. Thompson of Elberton can vouch for this. When he was young, his fiancée decided he was too poor to marry so she broke the engagement and sent back the gifts the doctor had given her. That *used* to be the custom. Among the gifts was a manicure set.

Nicee, an old Negro woman, cleaned Dr. Thompson's office each morning. "Nicee," he said, "here is a Christmas gift for you. It's a manicure set."

She took it, turned the leather case over and over without opening it. She looked at it fearfully. "Whut you say it is?"

"It's a manicure set."

Nicee handed it back to Dr. Thompson and said, "I don't want nothin' about it. You take it."

A man who had been around for a long span of years went to a doctor in Athens. He told the doctor that his left leg was hurting. The doctor said, "You must admit you've just got some age on you."

"Yes, Doctor, I know that, but this right leg is the same age as the left one and it ain't hurtin'."

—Louise Brown

"Why, Nicee, this is the first time you've ever refused a gift from me."

"This'n is different, Doctor. Jest to tell you the plumb full truth, I don't want to be cured of no man."

1980

Digging into the Past

Down in South Fulton County around the Palmetto area, I was asked to come and look at some Civil War letters and photographs. I drove up at the appointed hour all dressed up in a white linen skirt and green blazer. I had a meeting later and it was spring. I was met at the driveway and I was told, "Follow me."

As we passed the back porch my friend reached down and picked up a hoe and handed it to me saying, "Come with me." I thought she had buried the letters and photos. At the back of the house she said, "Honey, I've been wanting to plant my shasta daisies for some time now, so if you'll just dig the holes, I'll plant them."

I dug twelve holes without a word of protest. She was a very tall lady, and I'm sure she would have made a great sergeant in one of the wars. After planting her daisies we did go on to look at the material. Great material.

As I drove away waving goodby to her I thought, I'm sure glad I didn't get here at milking time.—Patsy Wiggins

The Gentle Art

I cannot say when the age of maturity comes, but surely by now with my years piled high, I can see the danger of telling it like it is.

One morning Lottie came into the office all choked up with a cold.

"How are you?" she sniffed.

"Terrible," I said, "just terrible. I have another catch in my back. I also have a ———."

Lottie interrupted me with a spasm of coughing and left the room. Later I met her in the hall and asked her how she felt.

"Fine," she coughed, "I never felt better."

"Lottie, you liar, you *know* you've got a cold."

"You're right," Lottie agreed, "but don't you know by now that nobody in the world wants to know how you *really* feel?"

That jolted me. My operations marched in front of me. Maybe all these years I hadn't exactly held my audience spellbound.

I became more and more curious about situations involving the whole truth, so I decided I would keep my eyes and ears wide open.

I had bought a dress that was, to put it mildly, a bit unusual. It had a simple front but the bustle in the back was a little more than unexpected. Papa was reading the evening news when I modeled my dress.

"How do you like it?" I asked.

Papa pondered. "Do you like it?"

"Yes, I do."

Dr. Rosalie Walston, former professor of English and chairman of the department at Georgia College, Milledgeville, was impressed when she saw two bumper stickers on a Milledgeville car. On one bumper sticker: God is my co-pilot. On the other: In case of emergency call 911.

"Well," he said, "if you like it I like it."

So I came to another conclusion. Truth can be veiled on the home front, especially when your back is turned.

The word *weight* is tricky. After contributing to the church building fund our minister was sufficiently kind to say that our weight was felt in the community. But after this ministerial pat on the back of a gullible human, I tried out a new roll recipe which did not turn out exactly as promised. As a guest picked up a roll that I had considered my masterpiece, she observed, "This *does* have weight."

More on more I can see the value of the veiled word. It contains charity and safety. There can, however, be a better plan.

The gentle art of silence.

1976

Ed Mims Remembers . . .

Uncle Uley

In July when the crops were laid by and there was little farm work to be done, it was customary to have a series of protracted meetings.

Brother Norman preached every night at a church that had a magnificent chancel rail and beautifully turned balusters.

One of Brother Norman's parishioners was Uncle Uley, a highly respected and dearly loved member of the community. Uncle Uley didn't and wouldn't go to church, even though Brother Norman had tried for years to get him to attend.

On this particular night, in walked Uncle Uley, and he walked down the aisle and sat in one of the front pews.

Brother Norman, sensing victory, quit preaching and asked if anyone would like to say a few words of prayer. It was easy. All you had to say was *pray*, and old Miz Campbell and others would jump up and start praying.

After several prayers Brother Norman said, "Uncle Uley, wouldn't you like to say a few words of prayer?"

Uncle Uley rose, went forward and kneeled before the chancel rail and started praying. Several times he stopped to catch his breath. His body moved from side to side, his arms began to quiver, and his voice got weaker and weaker.

Finally Uncle Uley said, "Brother Norman, for the Lord's sake, come down here and git my head out from between these posts."

For Seaborn Jones

The Lord had been good to them and blessed them with good rains and a bountiful crop. The Campbells wanted to show their appreciation and they invited the preacher, Reverend Seaborn Jones, to eat dinner with them after the service. The Reverend was noted for his long sermons, and on this day he held forth until near 12:30. When they got to the family home it was after one o'clock.

In the meantime Granny, who was left at the house to look after the kids and prepare the dinner, had set the table for noon. As was their custom,

Back in the old days in Georgia, church-going folks often referred to church commitment as making a proposition. One night at the Dewy Rose Baptist Church the preacher made a proposition that all those who wanted to go to heaven to stand up. Noticing that Gartrell Brown didn't stand up, the preacher asked, "Brother Gartrell, don't you want to go to heaven?"

"I'm in no hurry," said Brother Gartrell.

—Easton Brown

the kids were going around and around the table picking up tidbits until the roasted turkey was just about annihilated.

When the Campbells and Reverend Jones arrived, it seemed there was nothing else to do but proceed with the dinner. The mother asked the preacher to bless the food. Reverend Jones looked things over and bowed his head and said:

> God bless the owl
> Who picked the fowl
> And left the bones
> For Seaborn Jones!

Lee Mobley

Lee Mobley was a pretty good-size farmer, but his main occupation was sitting on the front porch reading the *Savannah Morning News*. As my father and I were going past the house, Lee saw my father, and he threw the paper down and jumped off the porch.

"Looka here, Doc," he said, "I just read in the paper that fish is a brain food. There ain't a word of it so. Gus Ponds ain't fed his chillun nothin' but fish all their lives and there ain't nary one got any sense."

Don't Worry, Doc

My father delivered the ninth child to a family, and after several days he inquired about the child's name.

"Boaz" he asked, "when are you going to name that baby? I need it for the birth certificate."

"Don't worry, Doc," Boaz replied. "We sent off to Sears, Roebuck for a name."

Burying Uncle John

Uncle John was the patriarch of the clan. Having lived some eighty-five years he died peacefully. As was the custom in the Low Country, the funeral lasted from noon until six or seven o'clock or until everybody got through visiting.

This was a special occasion since Uncle John was a storyteller, a banjo picker, and a sort of cornstalk preacher, as well as being a good dentist. Those attending the funeral came from Low Country, Green Pond, Yamassee, and down into south Florida.

One of the mourners was a nephew, Carew Rice, who had attained some fame as a cartoonist with big papers and later in life as a silhouette cutter.

There being a multitude of kids running, playing, singing, whooping and hollering, my Aunt Sally, Uncle John's wife, said to her daughter, "Emma, get them younguns and put 'em in that station wagon and find Carew and put him in with 'em so he can cut silhouettes and keep 'em quiet so we can get Uncle John properly buried."

My Father

My father, Frank Mims, was a country doctor. We lived on a large farm in the Over the Creek section of Screven County, which at that time was a rather isolated area.

For quite awhile when I was very young I was under the impression that Halley's Comet was named for me. I was born September 17, 1910, and I was named Harold Harber Martin. My grandpa Talmon Harber nicknamed me Halley. The word got around in Commerce and Homer that Halley's Comet was named for old man Talmon Harber's grandson.

—Harold Martin

Coming from a country store, my father was making his daily rounds, and he passed by a house where he had looked after all the family's illnesses and sick kids, and there had never been any mention of paying the doctor. No charges were ever put on the book. On this particular day my father decided to pass the farmer up, but the farmer rushed out and flagged him down.

"Doc," he said, "I've been waitin' to pay somethin' on my bill."

My father was very much impressed and puzzled over the man's decision.

My father said to his daughter, "Run down and git them chickens and bring them to Dr. Frank."

The child obeyed and appeared around the corner with two frizzly chickens with their legs tied together.

"Well," said my father, as he looked at the chickens, "I don't generally allow but fifteen cents for a chicken, but a frizzly chicken is worth fifty cents any time."

In Absentia

One thing is certain. You can be absent from school provided you have a reason, and the reason does not necessarily have to be reasonable.

Of course the attendance officer may attend to any discrepancy in the written excuse, but the consequences of invalidity do not always arouse enough fear to assure regular attendance.

Ten-year-old Beverly Buttons wrote her own excuses for being absent. She let so many kinfolks die that it became a grave problem. To think that a young girl would be subjected to so many losses at such a tender age! Strangely the deaths usually occurred on the Florida coast. In order to attend the services of the deceased, the family went by Camper Special and attached a contrivance that carried a contraption that could be used on the water—a seafaring vehicle you might say. At least it was attuned to the water and the possibility that fish might also succumb—to the right kind of lure.

This continued until Beverly exterminated an uncomfortable number of aunts, uncles, grandparents, great-grandparents and some rather distant cousins. According to Beverly's excuses, her mother and father were often victims of mysterious and deadly diseases, but somehow, in preparation for the customary demise, they managed to recover in time to navigate the Camper Special to points south.

The hobby of collecting handwritten excuses may dispel teacher fatigue more quickly than a high potency vitamin. For example: "We went on a business trip. It was my father's busness."

"I gave my child a puggative and it teamed out."

"I did not do my homework and who wants to take the wrap."

"Maria had a soar throat. It heart to much to make the trip to school."

"My child has a nervious stomache. It gets to shimmying when she can't do her nombers."

"We gave out of gas. It was three miles to the nearest filanstayshun."

Johnny James admitted that he wrote his own explanation for being absent from school. "Johnny's thooth aked. He kudnt kum." The teacher

When someone asked my cousin Marion Simmons how much she weighed Marion replied, "I'm exactly the right weight for my height, age, and social position."

—Julia Starke Harris

cast a sympathetic look at the young boy's swollen jaw. A jawbreaker on one side and bubble gum on the other.

Another articulate excuse was placed on the teacher's desk. "I fell down and broosed my rump. Any knitwit would stay home." Teacher's note: Wouldn't you too?

Young William Tuttle presented his teacher with the following information: "The school nurse sed William had to take a bath and have clean clothes if he came to school. It's not Sarrady and that's not your bizness I'll have you no."

This excuse came from a distraught mother: "My child did not feel like coming. My husband is a stalemate."

Mackie McDuffie just told it like it was. "When I play ball two or three nights a week and practice the other afternoons and nights I'm too tired to get up. Wouldn't you be?" The teacher agreed with a yawn.

A boy and his dog are not easily separated. "I came to school and my collie followed me. The principal wouldn't let my dog stay at school so I took him home and stayed with him."

A twelfth-grader explained his absence: "I didn't feel like coming. My girl had a date with my best friend."

Emphasis on thrift sometimes pays off. Susie Simpson wrote: "I went with my mama to but some money in the bank." When Susie was not admonished for her absence her teacher received a gift that money cannot buy. A most familiar scribbling: "Dod blass you. I love you bitter than my hot lunch."

Tillie Titchkin told the truth. "My mama's car warms up in the afternoon but it won't crank in the morning." Obviously Mama's car was not aligned to intellectual pursuit.

One first-grader refused to attend school because he didn't have the money to contribute to the tuberculosis drive. When he did appear he handed his teacher fifty cents. He said: "I didn't come yesterday because I didn't have the money for everybody who has a TV."

So—who can say if it is better to be punctual in school attendance? When someone stays away he just might be trying to help humanity.

But there is *one* thing a teacher can learn from these excuses: *Spilling shud be but hi on the kurrikulum. It realy shud.*

1974

There may not be so much to do in a little town but what you hear makes up for it.

—Betsy Auld Grinstead

Stacy Roberts Remembers . . .

The Perfect Picture

Once when I was a young man, I had a picture made by Mr. Taylor, an Elberton photographer. He was a painstaking perfectionist, and since he approved of the picture, he enlarged it and put it in a shop window for display purposes.

A friend of mine, noted for his bluntness, said, "Stacy, that picture surely does flatter you."

Mr. Taylor listened. He was not a man geared for too much talk, but he tuned in his ear. He took a careful look at the picture. Then he took an equally careful look at the blunt young man.

"Remember this," the photographer advised. "Never say a picture flatters a person. Just say the picture speaks well of a person in his absence."

Rube Phillips

Rube Phillips put Tom Watson high on a pedestal. Rube couldn't see, and he had a friend named Bud Smith who would read to him.

"Bud," Rube said, "let's read the *Jeffersonian*."

Bud said, "No, Rube, not this time. We'll read something else for a change." So he read awhile.

Rube started fidgeting. "Bud, don't read any more. What you're reading is a lie. It's enough to make my hair turn green."

Bud started laughing. "You know, Rube, I just read to you the living words of Tom Watson in the *Jeffersonian*."

Rube was quiet long enough to do some ruminating. Then he said, "Bud, I don't know but what old Tom ain't right after all."

Bishop Chandler

Bishop Warren Chandler drove a horse and buggy during his circuit rider days. When members of one of his churches presented him with a new car, he cranked it up and crashed into a picket fence. One of the church members asked, "Can I get you something?"

"Yes," Bishop Chandler replied. "Just give me a bundle of hay for a bungling jackass."

The Alien Card

Years ago a woman went into the Elberton post office and requested an *alien* card. Harry Cleveland, assistant postmaster asked, "What foreign country were you born in?"

The woman said, "I was born in the Flatwoods, but I've been ailin' the past six months."

The Talk of the Town

A story about a lady's downfall has been told many a time in Elberton. When Thornton Brothers' Grocery Store used to be on the public square in Elberton, it was a favorite place for men to meet and watch the crowds go by. One day, as usual, several men were congregated in front of the grocery store. When a lady approached the store her drawers fell down to her ankles. As she stepped out of them and picked them up she said with an edge of regret, "And to think they were my oldest pair."

You Figure It Out

as recalled and told by Jack McConnell

I have always enjoyed a joke or story that had a humorous twist but somehow didn't quite make sense after it settled in on you. With that in mind I'll share these two stories.

A fellow came into a local restaurant, sat down at the counter and ordered a glass of water and a BC headache powder. I was sitting next to

No sense in having a dog and barking yourself.

—Kathleen Meadow Brown

him and overheard the waitress ask, "Do you have a headache, Ben?"

"No," was the reply, "but if I get one I'll already have taken my BC!"

Another time traveling in the North Georgia mountains, I stopped for a hamburger and Coke at a small restaurant in Clayton. The waitress came, and I ordered my burger. She asked, "Do you want it with onions?"

"No, without," I said, and then she left for the kitchen, and I sat back to sip my Coke and wait for my burger to arrive. I overheard a loud conversation from the kitchen, and the waitress soon returned and said to me in a distressed voice, "The cook says you'll have to have it without something else. We ain't got no onions!"

Sunday Dinner

as recalled and told by Thad Stevens

A long time ago, Preacher Coile often came to eat with us on Sunday. The grownups ate at the first table and we younguns had to wait. We stuck our heads around the corner of the kitchen toward the dining room and watched them eat. We wondered if they'd leave us even a chicken wing.

"Brother Coile," Ma would say, "won't you have another piece of chicken?"

"Yes, ma'am, it hits the palate just right. I believe I'll have another portion."

After Preacher Coile said he'd have another portion for the third time, my brother asked, "Thad, what's a portion?" I replied, "Brother, from the looks of it, it's durn near all of it."

A still tongue makes a wise head.

—Jessie Banks

About the Author

Jannelle Jones McRee was born in Elberton, Georgia, the daughter of Jannie Oglesby and Walter Campbell Jones, both members of pioneer families of Elbert County. Jannelle attended Georgia State College for Women in Milledgeville and later was graduated from the University of Georgia in Athens.

For the past fifty years she has successfully pursued two careers: writing and teaching. She has taught school in Thomasville, Sandersville, Elberton, and East Point. For several years she worked for the *Elberton Star* as reporter and columnist, and for a number of years she was a special staff writer for the *Anderson Independent*. She also wrote many stories for Angus Perkerson, founding editor of the *Atlanta Journal Magazine*.

Jannelle served as editorial assistant on the staff of *Georgia Magazine* and later was assistant to the editor of *Georgia Life*. Appointed church historian, she wrote the history of St. Matthew Methodist Church in East Point, of which she is a charter member. She is active in writers' groups and civic organizations.

She is married to Roy L. McRee, and they divide their time between their home in East Point, Georgia, and the old family home in Elberton, which is listed on the National Register of Historic Places.

Index